Next Generation
Physician–Health System
Partnerships

Next Generation
Physician – Health System
Partnerships

CRAIG E. HOLM

 Health Administration Press | Chicago, Illinois

04 03 02 01 00   5 4 3 2 1

Library of Congress Cataloging-in-Publication Data

Holm, Craig E., 1954-
    Next generation physician, health system partnerships/Craig E. Holm.
        p. cm.
    Includes bibliographical references and index.
    ISBN 1-56793-124-3 (pbk. : alk. paper)
    1. Hospital-physician relations—United States. 2. Integrated delivery of health care—United States. 3. Hospital-physician joint ventures—United States. I. Title.
    RA971.9. H65 2000
    362.1'1'068—dc21

                                                            99-089952
                                                                CIP

The paper used in this publication meets the minimum requirements of American National Standards for Information Sciences—Permanence of Paper for Printed Library Materials, ANSI Z39.48–1984. ∞ ™

Health Administration Press
A division of the Foundation of the
    American College of Healthcare Executives
One North Franklin Street, Suite 1700
Chicago, IL 60606-3491
312/424-2800

Contents

Acknowledgments

THIS IS MY first and may be my only book. I never intended to write a book. However, I have a competitive nature, and after my father Bart and my partner Alan Zuckerman published books, I had no other alternative than to find a topic worth writing about.

Over the past two decades, I have observed the many mistakes made here in Philadelphia and in many other markets as integration models for hospitals, health systems, and physicians have emerged. Successes have been few. Unfortunately, a core set of integration models have been replicated throughout the country like computer viruses. Successful, sustainable partnership models seems a topic worth writing about.

Throughout the researching and writing of this book, I have been grateful to many people. First are my early mentors, the healthcare faculty of Cornell University who challenged me with lofty goals. Second, I thank my clients, many of whom participated in the development of this book. Third are my current and former colleagues of Health Strategies & Solutions, Inc., a firm in which we take great pride. I am particularly appreciative of my colleagues Hugo Finarelli, Joseph Spallina, and Alan Zuckerman, who set loftier goals than most of my professors and clients. Thank you Susan Arnold, my book editor, who toiled long hours to render the concepts readable to others.

Most importantly, thanks to my wife and professional colleague Kare and kids Shannon, Spencer, and Connor, who have taught me the reason for a real work ethic.

Craig E. Holm

1

The Challenges of
Physician–Health System
Partnerships

PHYSICIANS AND HOSPITALS have long coexisted as the key players in the healthcare delivery system. Relationships between them have been characterized by bonds of codependency, ranging from fierce independence to loose collaborations to complete hospital acquisition of physician practices. Each side has struggled with the harsh reality that neither can thrive without the existence and support of the other.

Physician-hospital affiliations have experienced variable success through the years as the effectiveness of a wide spectrum of models has been tested, largely driven by the potential for securing financial viability. In many cases, hospitals and health systems have pursued affiliations with physicians with the goal of maintaining their existing infrastructure and retaining or increasing referrals. These initiatives have had the appearance of trying to shelter physicians from the maelstrom of upheaval in the

1

industry but have often proved to be control mechanisms that reflect little foresight and understanding of what physicians want and need or of the long-term effects of the affiliation for both parties.

Physicians' avid interest in maintaining autonomy over clinical decisions while securing their financial futures is nurtured by the value of their decisions to patients' well-being and the many years of training their profession demands. Clinical autonomy and income disputes have challenged many physician-hospital partnerships—partnerships that must be grounded by the inevitability that the days of lucrative reimbursement and control of the reimbursement process are long gone. Physicians' entrepreneurial nature and their interests in more and better technology and equipment, ample time off, and convenient, accessible facilities have also been factors in the ongoing search for effective physician–health system partnerships.

As conflicts have intensified, a divisive wedge has been driven between physicians and hospitals. But a new urgency is now evident as competition among providers, battles with managed care companies, struggles for market share, tensions between primary care physicians and specialists, and threats from Wall Street–funded, for-profit management corporations have led to all-out warfare to see who will control or be on the receiving end of shrinking provider payments.

Hospitals will not be successful without solid, economically beneficial partnerships with physicians, because physicians control 75 percent of all medical costs within hospitals (Rutledge 1996). The physicians' pivotal position necessitates that physicians take a leading role in balancing the issues of cost, quality, and access in the realigning healthcare system.

As hospitals and physicians strive to provide quality care, the advantages afforded by affiliation and, ultimately, integration, can no longer be ignored. According to the Center for Research in Ambulatory Healthcare Administration (Managed Care

Information Center 1998), by the year 2000, most hospitals and medical groups will have ventured into integrated delivery systems or networks. The study predicts that the number of medical groups that are freestanding will drop from 87 percent in 1994 to 3 percent in 1999. The number of freestanding hospitals is predicted to drop from 78 percent to 5 percent in the same period (Managed Care Information Center 1998).

To make the most of shrinking reimbursement and valuable community resources and to survive in the next century of healthcare, physicians and hospitals must resolve conflicts and maximize areas of confluence and commonality by collaborating to integrate healthcare services and economic interests. Demands for cost efficiency and measurable outcomes will force hospitals and physicians to overcome their long histories of independence and, at times, dissension and find common ground that will enable them to align into mutually beneficial partnerships and integrated, financially successful systems and networks.

HISTORICAL PERSPECTIVE: HOW DID WE GET HERE?

Relationships between physicians and hospitals have historically been based upon the fundamental premises of independence and separatism. Medical practices were viewed as small, cottage industries and hospitals as large, community-based industries.

During the last 30 years of the twentieth century and particularly during the final decade, physician-hospital relationships nationwide evolved into a curious mix of marginally successful and financially disastrous partnerships.

Hospitals and physicians in the 1970s could be characterized as coexistent and independent—faculty practice plans and hospital-based physicians (e.g., pathologists, radiologists, emergency medicine physicians) were the only common examples of physicians who had been integrated into a system. By the late 1970s, however, early signs of competition emerged as warnings were heeded that the long-standing fee-for-service and cost-plus-reimbursement system might be challenged and that competition for healthcare dollars would increase.

During the 1980s, the notion that physicians and hospitals should consider more formal linkages spurred early integration efforts as competition among providers to align with physician practices intensified. The "alphabet soup" mix of physician-hospital alliances emerged as hospital-linked IPAs (independent practice associations), PHOs (physician-hospital organizations), MSOs (management service organizations), and hospital-affiliated GPWWs (group practices without walls) made their way into healthcare slang.

Intense competition for decreasing reimbursement has kept healthcare lawyers, accountants, and consultants busy in the 1990s. The organization of megagroups of physicians, formation of large integrated delivery systems, practice acquisition by health systems, the emergence of closer relationships between physicians and physician practice management and pharmaceutical firms, closure of some hospital medical staffs, and the influence of managed care companies have essentially left physicians with two choices: full integration with a hospital or health system (e.g., practice acquisition and exclusive contracting) or independence. The few options available in between full integration and independence, such as PHOs, discussed more fully in chapter 2, have failed to fulfill their promises of providing added value to physicians. Instead, such options often nearly irretrievably damage relationships between physicians and hospitals and leave a legacy of mistrust and jockeying and posturing for control.

The late 1990s witnessed the extent to which physicians have felt frustrated and angered by integrated delivery system and managed care dominance. In June 1999, the American Medical Association (AMA) voted to approve a national union for employed physicians (Reuters Health 1999). The plan authorizes the AMA to establish local negotiating units for physicians in training and hospital medical staff physicians and will affect about 100,000 employed physicians. Private practice physicians are currently not permitted to join unions or to have unions negotiate for them, but the AMA is backing federal and local legislation to remove this restriction and allow the AMA union to offer its services to self-employed physicians (Reuters Health 1999). State and regional organization efforts are currently underway.

CULTURE CLASH

While environmental forces have driven and molded many physician-hospital alliances and affected their degree of success, the vastly divergent cultural backgrounds that physicians and healthcare executives have brought to the bargaining table have also profoundly influenced the structure of the partnerships and their potential for success.

Physicians are highly autonomous and individualistic. Even in group practices they regard themselves as individuals tied together by centralized clinical and management systems (Barnett 1998). Physicians tend to exhibit healthy skepticism and be critical of themselves and others, and their loyalty typically lies with their patients and physician colleagues with whom they have worked for years. In contrast, physicians' relationships with hospital leaders are far more tenuous — a result, in part, of the shorter tenure of hospital administrative staff. Mistrust and concern over control often characterize physician views of hospital and healthcare system leaders, because the skills that have allowed a hospital to run profitably and effectively have not always been successful in meeting the needs and managing the operations of physician partnerships.

Further evidence of this "culture clash" is found in the training backgrounds of those ultimately responsible for physician practices (i.e., physicians) and those primarily responsible for hospital systems (i.e., hospital administrators). Physicians are trained in clinical practice, which demands decision making and management skills that are quite different from those of their hospital administrator colleagues. Understanding these differences helps provide insight into the challenges of developing meaningful and lasting partnerships.

Characteristics of Self-Employed Physicians

According to data from the AMA Socioeconomic Monitoring System (AMA 1998), the number of patient care physicians who are employees has risen fairly rapidly, increasing from 29 percent to 54 percent between 1983 and 1997. Despite this increase, many physicians remain self-employed (i.e., in private practice) and often exhibit many of the characteristics presented below.

- Physicians work independently. Until recently most physicians were leaders of one-physician practices and had a total of two to five employees. Interaction with hospitals was periodic and sporadic, and included such activities as continuing education and other professional relationships, some of which were required for staff privileges and clinical referral relationships. Academic medical center faculty and hospital-based physicians (e.g., anesthesiologists, pathologists, radiologists, and emergency department physicians) are common exceptions that are discussed later in this chapter.
- Physicians make clinical decisions affecting individual patients and business decisions involving only three to six people. The vast majority of decisions made by physicians are clinical and involve individuals and specific disease conditions. Business decisions in physician practices usually lack great complexity when compared to those made in the hospital environment, and affect only a few staff members.

- Physicians make decisions quickly based on the information available. Clinical decisions are made fairly rapidly to accelerate the healing or preventive health process. Although diagnostic tests aid in decision making, a clinical judgement or diagnosis sometimes must be based on less than complete information to expedite decision making about the appropriate treatment plan. It is often appropriate to render a diagnosis quickly based on the availability of the vast majority of the information than to delay a treatment plan until all of the desired information is available. The available timeframe for decision making may be quite short.

- Physicians lack business or management training. Medical school training focuses on the scientific origin of disease and clinical diagnosis and treatment. Training in business and practice development is virtually non-existent, and is usually gained through "on-the-job" experiences.

- Physicians work in an entrepreneurial, small business environment. Physicians in private practice have the ultimate motivation: to make their practice succeed to protect their personal livelihood, reputation, and status. However, the complexity and magnitude of the variables influencing a successful practice are few in comparison to those that lead to the success or failure of a hospital system. Solo practices usually generate between $200,000 and $750,000 in revenue annually, compared to a hospital system often with annual revenue of several hundred million dollars.

- Physicians often lack consensus-building skills. Because of the small size of many physician practices and the nature of solo leadership, physicians rarely have a chance to develop or test consensus-building skills. Most clinical decisions are made quickly with limited information. In contrast, developing consensus is time-consuming and usually requires thorough investigation of all components of the situation and the underlying rationale is explored from every imaginable perspective to satisfy as many of the affected constituents as possible.

Characteristics of Hospital Administrators

In contrast, hospital administrators are often responsible for one component or for all of a multimillion-dollar business enterprise. Their training, professional behavior, and work environment are usually a striking contrast to that of the typical physician in private practice.

- Hospital administrators facilitate consensus decision making. Most hospital systems are made up of 30 to 40 individual departments, many of which have oversight by a professional manager and a clinical (often a physician) leader. For most major hospital system decisions (e.g., whether to merge or affiliate, development of new programs, development of an annual capital budget), multiple departments are affected and vast resources and professional talent are usually available. In general, to successfully manage a complex enterprise, such as a hospital, administrators must obtain as much input as possible to facilitate consensus decision making.
- Administrators require a comprehensive analysis of the rationale, implications, and process for an issue or problem before making a decision. The reason behind this behavior is linked to the preceding point. Such an approach enables the hospital administrator to make progress in gaining consensus regarding a particular issue, but it also renders the process slow and laborious

as every new angle is explored and every approach to an issue is examined. As a result, hospital administrators have a reputation for making decisions slowly and exhibiting bureaucratic behavior. Physicians view this behavior as administrators being unable to make decisions on their own. In reality administrators usually attempt to wait to build consensus and analyze the situation in a comprehensive manner before coming to a conclusion and making a recommendation. However, the health-care market early in 2000 requires more expeditious decision making. Complete consensus building has become a luxury. Increasingly, decisions are financially driven rather than based predominantly on consensus.

- Administrators work in teams and primarily in meetings. Patients arrive at a physician's office, are examined by a physician, and depart with a diagnosis and treatment plan. In contrast, hospital administrators conduct most of their business day in a group setting and rely on the power of persuasion, thorough analyses, and convincing arguments to sway others toward a specific course of action. Usually, very little progress toward furthering the course of action occurs in between each meeting.

- Administrators gain extensive business and management training through graduate-level education and hospital management continuing education. The typical training of a hospital administrator is a liberal arts or business undergraduate degree followed by several years of experience and then a two-year graduate program focusing on business or healthcare administration. The hospital administrator then participates in ongoing training in the business approach to healthcare at continuing education seminars. In addition, the administrator often has a supervisor who prepares a professional development plan, including participation in targeted continuing education programs.

- Administrators make business decisions that involve many. The administrator, after a comprehensive evaluation of the issues involved, will eventually make or facilitate a decision. Part of the rationale for involving so many people in the input stages of processing an issue is to ensure that constituencies affected will not be surprised and that they will support the implementation process. Although superiors overturn some decisions by hospital administrators, this rarely happens in the physician practice environment where the physician is the "captain of the ship."

Clearly, the operating environments and cultures of the two groups differ greatly in style, have led to miscommunication and a lack of trust between physicians and hospitals, and have engendered separatism rather than partnerships. However, exceptions to the rule of absolute independence of physicians and hospital systems have occurred, mostly prior to 1990, and varying levels of integration have been achieved. Three of these exceptions are outlined below.

1. Faculty–academic medical center relationship. In this relationship, physicians are employed, usually through a faculty practice plan, to practice within the confines of the organization's academic mission, including education, research, and clinical responsibilities. Often these employed faculty physicians earn tenured, professional status similar to other university faculty. However, these relationships are limited to a relatively small subset of physicians, usually subspecialty physicians whose focus is predominantly teaching or research instead of clinical practice. This exception is generally successful

because of the confluence of objectives, notably the shared pursuit by all parties of the academic mission: research, teaching, and clinical care.

2. Physician relations programs. These programs, which exhibit some level of affiliation and collaboration but not necessarily a partnership, continue to be fairly common in the industry. The concept is for personal visitation to physician practices by a hospital management representative (often called a "physician sales representative"). The formal agenda for the visit was historically, "How can ABC Hospital support your practice?" The hidden agenda for these visits was "How can ABC Hospital garner some, all, or more of your inpatient and ancillary referral volumes?" These programs have been prevalent as vehicles for addressing a major source of conflict between health systems and physician practices—unresolved or unattended hospital operations inefficiencies.

3. Employment or practice acquisition by a hospital system. Before the flurry of primary care physician employment in the 1990s, employment of physicians was mostly limited to hospital-based specialists (e.g., anesthesiologists, radiologists, emergency medicine physicians, intensivists, and pathologists). Often a limited number of other specialists whose practices included a substantial portion of hospital-linked care also had some sort of contractual relationship with a hospital system. Examples of these contractual relationships include medical directorship of medicine or surgery; the intensive care unit; the pathology, emergency medicine, or radiology departments; the vascular laboratory; and the hospital-based gastrointestinal laboratory. The logic for developing these contractual relationships has been to secure and stabilize coverage in those specialties that support all

other specialties practicing at the hospital and to pay a stipend in some cases to offset losses in clinical practice revenue resulting from administrative responsibilities. This approach has been used extensively by hospitals because it provides a major area of confluence: hospitals' desire for coverage and physicians' desire for secure, contractual relationships.

These and many other strategies (e.g., MSOs, joint contracting, joint ventures) have been employed to integrate physicians; however, independence has historically been the most common state for physician practices. Hospitals have relied on the attraction of technology and equipment and the loyalty of physicians to focus their practice at a particular hospital. In such a relationship, physicians work in a hospital, refer to a hospital's programs and services, refer to specialists who are affiliated with the hospital, and satisfy the medical staff membership requirements of hospital committee and meeting attendance.

Without formal ties, physicians can easily shift loyalties and practices from one hospital system to another. In Philadelphia, "the three Bs," three well-known orthopedists, Arthur Bartolozzi, Robert Booth, and Richard Balderston, left the Rothman Institute at Pennsylvania Hospital in July 1997 to join Allegheny Health System (Cohen 1999). The corporation owned by the three orthopedists was guaranteed $3.9 million a year in salary plus incentives. Allegheny also agreed to pay for all building upgrades, billing and support staff, and valet parking for patients (Stark 1998). One year later Allegheny filed for bankruptcy and the group took their 4,000 procedures per year back to Pennsylvania Hospital (Business News in Brief 1998).

To combat the potential loss of physicians, hospitals have employed various strategies in an attempt to "bind" physicians. Examples from the late 1980s and early 1990s include:

- Recruitment assistance. This service has typically included the payment (when legally warranted) of recruitment fees, reimbursement for moving expenses for new recruits, and loans for practice start-up expenses. Federal regulators (e.g., the Internal Revenue Service) seem to afford more latitude (so that hospitals do not jeopardize their tax-exempt status) if consideration of these payments is preceded by an evaluation of community need for physicians. The evaluation should objectively demonstrate that the hospital system is supporting, either in the present or projected for the future, the provision of incremental physician supply to an area of demonstrated community need.
- Designation of medical director positions. Sometimes a stipend is provided to a physician who is designated as medical director for a service. Examples include a quality assurance or utilization review medical director and medical director of a clinical program (e.g., cardiology, oncology, home care). The medical director stipend should be a legitimate fair market payment for work required. Such work includes committee meeting attendance, quality review of a program, and other responsibilities. These attempts have generally failed to secure the loyalty of physicians, as demonstrated by the high turnover rate of medical directors and the fact that the linkage is focused on a narrow topic rather than broad based.

PHYSICIAN–HEALTH SYSTEM PARTNERSHIPS IN A COMPETITIVE, MANAGED CARE ENVIRONMENT

The realities of the reimbursement environment have been felt full force by hospitals and health systems in the past five to seven years as physicians and hospitals are attempting to deal with the "common enemy"—managed care payors and their influences. A number of integration strategies, such as MSOs, PHOs, joint ventures, and IPAs, have been attempted to improve practice and health system visibility and have dramatically changed the relationships between hospital systems and physicians. These strategies (discussed more extensively in chapter 2) have experienced some marginal success but in most cases—such as practice acquisition and employment—have led to disastrous financial performance and strained relationships. The growing pains experienced by these physician-hospital relationships include governance and control battles, mistrust about the intentions of each party, huge operating losses, declines in physician productivity and morale, bloated cost structures, and, generally, failed promises.

Despite these failures, a number of compelling rationales remain for continuing to explore and create more effective physician-hospital partnerships:

- Hospitals and physicians are in the same business of healthcare, serving the same customers, in the same communities. Ideally, hospitals and physicians should share responsibility and accountability for the health status of communities they serve. Many potential physician partners represent entities from outside a community whose interests are profit motivated rather than community oriented.

- Hospitals' and physicians' strategic advantages are different but complementary—hospitals can certainly learn about entrepreneurship from physicians and physicians can benefit from hospitals' resources and clout.

- Competition between hospitals and physicians can be a deleterious use of valuable and often shrinking community resources. A common example is the proliferation of independent physician-owned ambulatory surgery centers that have duplicated resources available at hospital operating rooms.

- Physician-hospital partnerships have the potential to generate financial benefits for both parties, including improved market position from the more extensive development of programs and services, the ability to secure managed care contracts, and joint venture opportunities that can increase physician practice incomes while sustaining or maintaining hospital system revenue.
- Hospitals are motivated to create sustainable partnerships with physicians. Hospitals face threats from other hospitals, physician practice management firms, and payors who may attempt to partner with physicians and force hospitals into the role of a vendor or commodity rather than that of a vital component or driver of healthcare delivery in a community. Hospitals also fear that their "loyal" physicians will partner with "nonloyal" physicians.

Recently, more creative and meaningful relationships between systems and physicians have been emerging, and employment is not the only example of a fully integrated relationship. Relationships between physicians and hospital systems are evolving. The limited number of options thought to exist for hospitals and physicians has been expanded to include a variety of relationships that establish sustainable partnerships, provide value to both physicians and hospitals, and reduce conflict.

This book will examine these evolving relationships and how they affect both physicians and hospitals. How can hospitals and health systems avoid steep financial losses from physician affiliations? How can physicians benefit from partnerships with hospitals? How can partnerships be structured to enhance the clinical autonomy of physicians and stave off reductions in physician income? How can partnerships create value for the hospital, physicians, patients, and payors?

With increasingly compelling evidence that their futures are inextricably intertwined, hospitals and physicians must aggressively seek new and more creative models for working together — models that are grounded in trust and shared governance and are committed to managing care to enhance quality and control costs, rather than control referrals. In this volatile and unstable period in the healthcare industry, the risks of maintaining the status quo or letting past failures prevent future collaborations are high. Hospitals and physicians with a willingness to break new ground and create more effective alliances will set the standard for physician-hospital partnerships in the next century of healthcare and will become strong competitors in their markets.

REFERENCES

American Medical Association and the Center for Health Policy Research. 1998. *Socioeconomic Characteristics of Medical Practice 1997/ 98*, 18. Chicago: American Medical Association.

Barnett, A. E. 1998. "Public Physician Practice Management Companies." *Medical Group Management Journal* (May/June): 51.

Business News in Brief. 1998. *Philadelphia Inquirer* September 16: C3

Cohen, M. 1999. "Waiting for Bartolozzi." *Philadelphia Magazine* [Online article. Retrieval 5/14/99]. www.phillymag.com

Managed Care Information Center. 1998. *Top Trends in Physicians' Roles in an Integrated Healthcare Environment*, 2. Pamphlet. Manasquan, NJ: The Managed Care Information Center.

Reuters Health. 1999. "AMA OK's Union for Docs." [Online article. Retrieval 6/99]. www.news.excite.com.

Rutledge, V. R. 1996."Hospital/Physician Alignment: A Model for Success." *Oncology Issues* 11 (6): 18–20.

Stark, K. 1998. "Allegheny Culture: Privileges and Perks Bankruptcy Neared, But Salaries Soothed." *Philadelphia Inquirer* December 27: A01.

The "Disintegrating" Models of
Physician–Health System
Relationships

As the architects of integrated delivery systems have sought to bring physicians and hospitals into single organizational structures, there have been significant growing pains on all sides. According to the Medical Group Management Association, many of these new partnerships have evolved into "distressed marriages" that may be heading toward divorce (MGMA 1999). And solid evidence exists that creating these organizational structures in no way guarantees integration.

Each physician-hospital affiliation has encountered its own unique set of roadblocks, but common sources of difficulties underlie these alliances:

- Mistrust and lack of credibility among partners.
- Failure to commit fully to the partnership.
- Imbalances in control and power in the partnership.
  The prevailing stereotypes are of hospitals seeking

17

control of physicians and market dominance and physicians resisting integration and cannibalizing hospital revenues.

- Inability to achieve or demonstrate improved market position relative to other health systems or payors.
- Failure to delineate short-term and long-term goals and objectives of the partnerships.
- Overemphasis on and attention to relationships with primary care physicians to the exclusion of specialists.
- Failure to communicate expectations and concerns about the partnership.
- Overemphasis on short-term financial gains or losses and failure to keep sight of long-term strategic and financial objectives.
- Perceptions of favoritism and lack of objective criteria used to develop partnerships.
- Inability of hospitals to manage partnerships.
- Exclusion of physician leaders in the development and management of the partnership.
- Creation of partnerships as a competitive strike, often without thoughtful planning and under the rationale that if "we don't take action now, someone else will."
- Declines in physician productivity and morale.
- Disagreement over acceptable physician and hospital performance measures.

The early models of physician-hospital partnerships suffered from the mere fact that they were highly experimental, but these partnerships were also the victims of unrealistic expectations about joining together such diverse groups and getting physicians to buy into the value and need for partnerships. Many physician-hospital partnerships occurred in the flurry of activity associated with the perceived need to develop fully and tightly bound integrated delivery networks in the late 1980s and throughout the 1990s.

This chapter reviews the "disintegrating" models of physician–health system partnerships that have failed to deliver on their promises of market leverage, improved operational efficiencies and economies of scale, favorable positioning relative to competitors, and increased access to managed care contracts. Despite the shortcomings of these models, reviewing their successes and failures is a valuable exercise for understanding their potential as transitional models for future partnerships.

PRACTICE ACQUISITION

During the 1990s, a frenzy of physician practice acquisition occurred. Hospitals and health systems paid increasingly exorbitant sums for practices to lock in primary care physicians, protect their referral bases, and lay the foundations for integrated delivery systems. Commonly used rationales for acquisition included:

- "It's a defensive strategy" (i.e., in defense of acquisition by other hospital systems).
- "We will ensure referrals to our hospital, ancillary services, and subspecialist practices."
- "Having lots of primary care physicians is the only way to have any managed care clout."
- "If we build our base of primary care physicians, our hospital system will be an attractive candidate for potential system affiliates."
- "We can justify the losses incurred on acquired practices because primary care physicians bring in up to a million dollars per year in admissions and subspecialty referrals."

PRACTICE ACQUISITION: VIEWS FROM THE INDUSTRY

You are never going to get the hustle out of the doctor as an employee of any type like you did when he was working for himself.
—Stuart P. Brogadir, M.D., M.B.A., System Strategist
Elliot Health System, Manchester, New Hampshire

The old system of trying to prove that there is a benefit to owning a physician practice, even though it is losing $50,000 a year, is going by the wayside. In the future there simply isn't going to be $50,000 sitting out there to be lost. Some hospitals are going to die by virtue of implementing what they thought they had to do to survive. They have boxed themselves into a corner because they have sunk tens of millions of dollars into practice acquisition and employment and their profit margin cannot recoup that investment.
—Christopher Howard, Executive Vice President
Health*first* Inc., Oklahoma City, Oklahoma

One of our clients has a strategy that they're calling "Free Willy." They want the doctors that they have acquired to go back into the community and into private practice. The hospital doesn't want to own them or manage them, but they want them in the community. What this hospital has found is that the physicians didn't really

(continued on facing page)

Physicians have in many cases been extremely willing partners in the practice acquisition frenzy. From their perspective, practice acquisition often provides:

- A linkage to an entity (i.e., a hospital) with market clout;
- Immediate cash for retirement, investment, dependent education, or medical school loans;
- Salary guarantees in economically volatile markets;

change their practice patterns, where they practiced, where they admitted patients, or other things. So why pay all that money for market share that you already had and put yourself into a bad relationship with the physicians? The hospital was doing okay before in terms of hospital performance and having good relationships with their physicians, but they really didn't want to own them. Get out of that relationship, get the physicians back into the community, and see if you can help them in other ways.

    —D. Louis Glaser, Esq., Partner

      Gardner, Carton & Douglas, Chicago, Illinois

I have seen examples of practice acquisition working, but nine times out of ten, hospitals don't model the employment agreement correctly and the compensation model leads to the disaster that most hospitals are experiencing.

    —Adam Henick, Executive Director

      Montefiore Medical Group, New York, New York

We would rather be friends to all physicians while on staff instead of selectively owning and operating some practices and being in competition with physicians who are not on our staff.

    —Amit Mody, M.D., Regional Director of Planning

      St. Barnabas Health System, Livingston, New Jersey

- Better quality of life—the daily hassles of practice management are removed, fewer work hours are usually required, and on-call time is less frequent;
- Access to capital for future development of the practice; and
- Removal from managed care contracting battles.

In the acquisition model, a practice's assets are purchased. The assets may include hard assets (e.g., land, a building, medical and office equipment) and accounts receivable or intangible assets (e.g., patient lists, medical records, goodwill). The individual physician is responsible for his or her clinical care provided by the practice, and clinical decisions remain the responsibility of the individual physician.

The practice acquisition process involves completion of a practice valuation. The report usually includes a description of the practice, an assessment of the physical facility, a recommended practice purchase price based on projected earnings for the practice, and most important, recommended initiatives to help achieve incremental earnings to repay the practice acquisition investment to the purchaser.

With few exceptions the strategy of owning and managing physician practices has failed, and acquiring organizations pay steep prices to learn this difficult lesson. Physicians have not been as productive when employed by others as they have been when they must account for themselves (that is, when they are 100 percent at risk) or belong to a locally managed physician network (Barnett 1998). Perceived loss of autonomy, empowerment, and entrepreneurial spirit while working within a new and seemingly autocratic infrastructure; lack of hospital expertise in practice management; and the tendency of older physicians to view the sale of their practices as a means for cashing in for retirement are but a few reasons cited for the failure of this strategy.

The rush to move physicians from independent relationships to fully integrated acquisition and employment relationships has led to disastrous fiscal results, and hospitals and health systems show deep financial losses on their records as hard evidence of the failures of practice acquisition. Most acquired practices have failed to generate incremental earnings to recoup the purchase price of the investment and postacquisition practice costs usually far exceed preacquisition practice costs. Even more striking are the annual losses acquired practices are exhibiting. A study by Coopers & Lybrand found that hospitals lose, on average, $97,000 per physician per year for acquired practices, much of which results from inferior performance in volume, revenues, and costs ("Hospitals that Gobbled..." 1997). Hospital-owned groups bring in about $154,000 less in revenue per full-time equivalent (FTE) and $88,000 less in operating costs, but physicians working at hospital-owned practices earn only $1,100 less a year than independent practitioners (MGMA 1999). One reason for this discrepancy is that hospitals often provide salary guarantees for physicians without performance incentive plans. Hospital-owned practices also have higher overhead, at 65 percent compared with 55 percent for non–hospital-owned practices (Terry 1998).

The era of rampant practice acquisition and employment appears to be waning. Although many hospital systems are still acquiring practices, the activity has slowed. In Philadelphia, one of the "hotbeds" of practice acquisition and employment of physicians, the major health systems have begun significant downsizing of their networks of primary care physician practices, restructuring physician contracts into shorter terms, developing incentive-laden contracts, enacting other aggressive expense-reduction initiatives, and helping some of the employed physicians transition back into private practice.

The question now facing hospitals and health systems that own physician practices is how to stem the losses and develop sustainable, postacquisition relationships for the future. A major primary care network in the Northeast with projected operational losses that are substantial and ongoing is giving physicians two options: (1) go back into private practice with some funding to ease the transition; or (2) face aggressive monitoring and management by the sponsoring health system—measures such as office-hour requirements, emergency room call coverage and other new clinical responsibilities, support staffing reductions, and new incentive compensation arrangements.

Divestiture of acquired practices will be a painful process, but it will also lay the groundwork for establishing the next generation of physician–health system partnerships discussed in chapter 3.

TRADITIONAL PHOS

The first generation of physician-hospital organizations (PHOs), also referred to as traditional PHOs, are joint ventures between hospitals and members of their medical staffs that function as agents for negotiating managed care contracts. PHOs may also own or operate ambulatory care clinics or ancillary care facilities as well as provide administrative services for physician members. If the PHO is successful in obtaining contracts, its role may be expanded to process premiums paid by the insurer (Clapp and Jamieson 1997).

Open PHOs accept all members of a hospital's medical staff and thus tend to be dominated by specialists. Physicians usually retain ownership of their practices and pay an annual fee to fund the PHO's operating expenses. Ideally open PHOs are an opportunity for all physicians to be part of a larger contracting entity for a modest investment. However, the open PHO does not fundamentally change the physician practice to make it more competitive. In addition, even if the PHO is successful in obtaining a contract (and many are not), the PHO structure does not have a mechanism for managing the cost of care.

Closed PHOs are similar to open PHOs except that membership is limited to a select group of physicians that meet criteria for specified credentials or payor panel requirements, high quality, and cost-effectiveness. The structure's focus on exclusivity is intended to build an elite primary care base, but research indicates that even in closed PHOs more than 80 percent of the

---

TRADITIONAL PHOs: VIEWS FROM THE INDUSTRY

PHOs are empty contracting shells. Hospitals and health care systems have tried to use PHOs as platforms for working with physicians on managed care contracts, but many PHOs have no managed care infrastructure and fail outright to win contracts. Ultimately, PHOs add no value."

    —Lawton R. Burns, Ph.D., Professor of Health Care Systems
      The Wharton School, University of Pennsylvania,
      Philadelphia, Pennsylvania

---

medical staff may be members (The Advisory Board Company 1993). Closed PHOs can also drive a wedge between specialists on the medical staff, with excluded specialists often leaving the sponsoring hospital (Clapp and Jamieson 1997, 21–23). At best, a closed PHO represents a transition to more advanced partnerships.

PHOs have been touted for allowing providers to garner more contracts at better rates and establish leverage with payors while presumably improving collaboration and quality of care. However, from the perspective of many physicians, PHOs have simply run the same or fewer contracts for physician members, often at the same negotiated prices physicians would have received on their own. Meanwhile, physicians pay a surcharge to cover the cost of the PHO infrastructure that has provided little or no value. Other physician criticisms of PHO structures include:

- Hospitals invest heavily in PHOs and dominate decision making. Often hospitals "loan" PHOs funds for start-up and working capital costs, and sometimes these loans go unpaid.
- PHOs are often led by hospital executives with little knowledge of medical management and managed care contracting and administration.

- PHO information systems lack the abilities to measure and manage care and outcomes that are necessary when PHO contracts include risk assumption.
- PHOs tend to be dominated by specialists. Primary care physicians have watched the value of their practice linkage to a hospital increase and have seen little need for PHOs; however, given the financially devastating results of many primary care networks, primary care physicians and hospitals have the opportunity to work together through other vehicles. If these affiliations are unsuccessful, primary care physicians will likely turn to other partnerships that are independent of hospitals, such as, other physician practices or physician practice management companies.

TRADITIONAL MSOS

Management service organizations (MSOs) are mechanisms for providing physicians access to capital for practice growth and development and practice management, staffing, marketing, planning, research, and systems support (Clapp and Jamieson 1997, 21–23). The intent of MSOs is to provide access to the economies of scale that large organizations can offer. Member physicians then pay the MSO a percentage of collections, a fixed monthly fee, or fees based on a sliding scale. A number of different MSO structures exist, ranging from mergers of physician practices to complete buyouts by hospitals, other physicians, or publicly traded equity organizations (Clapp and Jamieson 1997, 21–23). The most common MSO structure is a service organization from which practices can purchase services such as billing and collections, employee benefits, contract evaluation, insurance, and medical supplies.

Traditional hospital-owned MSOs enable physicians to purchase practice management or support services at a fair market

TRADITIONAL MSOs: VIEWS FROM THE INDUSTRY

I have never found a role for traditional MSOs because they have usually been hospital enterprises with the goal of trying to get physicians to use their services. These services have never been distinctively excellent or well-priced.

—Stuart P. Brogadir, M.D., M.B.A., System Strategist
Elliot Health System, Manchester, New Hampshire

I have seen very few MSOs that provide value-added services. The value-added services they could be offering are information systems, because physician offices are woefully inadequate in that area. But few MSOs have true expertise with technology.

—Adam Henick, Executive Director
Montefiore Medical Group, New York, New York

Under the rubric of practice management, we don't do a better job in billing and collecting, so what is left—human resources or contract management? If a physician is board certified and generally practicing good, sensible, cost-effective medicine, they are going to get into most managed care contracts.

—Amit Mody, M.D., Regional Director of Planning
St. Barnabas Health System, Livingston, New Jersey

price, generally as a package deal, with physicians retaining clinical and financial autonomy. These MSOs generally focus on management and administration and not on marketing the practices for contracting purposes. Hospitals presumably improve relationships with physicians by using the MSO structure to increase practice revenue through improved collections and reduced practice operating costs through economies of scale. However, MSO administrators, generally hospital administrators with little knowledge of medical practice management or practice managers and little experience in directing large-scale, multispecialty practice organizations, have been unable to fulfill the promise of increased revenue. A 1997 survey of 140 hospital-sponsored MSOs revealed that only 11 percent of the respondents (one out of nine) were able to achieve break-even status. The remaining MSOs lost money (Medimetrix 1999). Inferior performance by hospital-sponsored MSOs is usually a result of poor billing and collections' performance, excessive staffing and compensation/benefit levels, and expensive facility costs. All lead to deleterious effects on practice financial performance.

Comprehensive MSOs purchase a group's assets (including tangible assets), manage its medical practice, and negotiate managed care contracts. The MSO then provides personnel management, administration, group purchasing, office leasing, and contracting. The physician group usually retains a separate legal identity (e.g., a professional corporation or "P.C.") and the responsibility for generating revenue. This model has the advantage of allowing physicians to benefit from an infusion of capital (from the purchase of the group's hard assets), while allowing the physicians to retain control over clinical practice, physician compensation, and governance. However, this model seems to be transitional as physicians, particularly primary care physicians, move on to models that more formally integrate their practices and allow them to negotiate and manage risk contracts (Clapp and Jamieson 1997, 21–23).

Equity MSOs are for-profit, private, or publicly traded structures that purchase tangible and intangible assets of physician practices. The MSO controls the revenue stream, taking a percentage off the top or paying the physicians at a set compensation level and keeping the balance. In return, the MSO manages the practices and negotiates managed care contracts, presumably in a superior manner.

Overall MSOs have failed to meet their financial objectives. *The Management Services Organization Benchmarking Survey: 1998 Report Based on 1997 Data* by the Medical Group

Management Association reports that MSOs are losing a median amount of $19,615 a year per FTE physician based solely on MSO corporate operations (Dunevitz 1998). But there are signs that MSOs may be making progress, particularly with operational efficiencies. The median amount of charges in accounts receivable per FTE is $70,974, compared to $82,220 for hospital-owned multispecialty group practices studied in another Medical Group Management Association survey (Dunevitz 1998). In addition, the use of utilization review and patient management mechanisms is increasing among MSOs that manage a significant amount of capitated contracts (Dunevitz 1998).

As MSOs move out of their infancy and adapt to market realities, a new generation of MSOs is emerging as a viable physician–health system partnership model. These MSOs are discussed in chapter 3.

GROUP PRACTICES WITHOUT WALLS

Group practices without walls (GPWWs) emerged to give physicians more clout as hospitals were aligning for market influence and payors were gaining ground in controlling reimbursement. GPWWs were also formed in response to Stark legislation that sought to stop referrals from physicians to ancillary providers with whom the physicians had financial ties. Prior to the Stark legislation, physicians in a geographic area would invest in imaging centers, laboratories, and other ancillary services and then refer all of their patients to these services (Clapp and Jamieson 1997, 21–23). Such services proved to be lucrative investments for physicians because a steady stream of patients was guaranteed. When the Stark legislation prohibited many of these arrangements, physicians still felt a need for convenient, accessible ancillary services for their patients, particularly in locations where other providers were unavailable. Using a single provider number, the loosely affiliated GPWWs allow physicians to share overhead expenses

---

GROUP PRACTICES WITHOUT WALLS: VIEWS FROM THE INDUSTRY

GPWWs are a nice concept that is certainly better than independent practices, but as the rubber hits the road, if we're really serious about providing cost-effective health care and realizing surpluses, there are still inefficiencies that will need to be addressed
by putting the physicians into the same walls.
　　　—Stuart P. Brogadir, M.D., M.B.A., System Strategist
　　　　Elliot Health System, Manchester, New Hampshire

I think under the proposed Stark revisions, GPWWs are probably a
nonfunctional entity.
　　　—Adam Henick, Executive Director
　　　　Montefiore Medical Group, New York, New York

---

and pursue managed care contracts without hospital involvement, while at the same time maintaining separate locations and
retaining decision-making powers within individual offices.

This model has proved to be an adequate approach for managing costs, especially for physicians who desire a high degree of
independence but want to benefit from the scale economies
achieved through some consolidated overhead. However, GPWWs
have not demonstrated significant market clout with payors, nor
the ability to achieve significant economies of scale, which are
the result of consolidating many practice overhead and support
functions. GPWWs may also become unattractive if an even more
restrictive regulatory environment emerges.

THE FOUNDATION MODEL

The foundation model is a not-for-profit corporation usually organized as a hospital affiliate or subsidiary that purchases physician
group practices. The physicians are organized into a separate

THE FOUNDATION MODEL: VIEWS FROM THE INDUSTRY

From the physician's perspective, I think most physicians feel threatened without the weight of a big organization to negotiate contracts. Physicians feel that foundations allow them to get away from the management of medicine and focus more on being doctors and seeing patients. From the hospital's perspective, there are disadvantages. Physicians who are not working for themselves are not as invested in financial quality or making ends meet. Physicians in a foundation may feel there are deep pockets out there, but it doesn't come from them. You also lose that kind of warm fuzzy touch of a smaller group when you start gathering together groups of 300 physicians. You lose a bit of the intimacy, collaboration, and core identity.

—Martin S. Lipsky, M.D., Professor and Chair
Department of Family Medicine
Northwestern University Medical School
Chicago, Illinois

I think foundations are a reasonable intermediate model between full practice acquisition and individual independent practices. It is a good way of getting tax-exempt debt and realizing some funding that would otherwise not be available. The foundation model also puts physicians in the position of deciding about allocation of resources, which I think is very constructive.

—Stuart P. Brogadir, M.D., M.B.A., System Strategist
Elliot Health System, Manchester, New Hampshire

corporate entity and sign a professional service agreement with the foundation. Foundations are characterized by high risk sharing and a high degree of exclusivity—physician employees are involved in all risk arrangements signed by the system and work exclusively for the parent organization (Dynan, Bazzoli, and Burns 1998).

This model is commonly viewed as the not-for-profit version of practice acquisition, particularly in states where direct employment of physicians is prohibited. As owner of the practices, the foundation can invest in the practices and allow physicians to share in the resulting revenue. The income levels of most foundation physicians can approximate those of private practice physicians. As not-for-profit entities, foundations are also able to retain some earnings in reserve. Foundations frequently only purchase the hard assets of physician practices, so the purchase prices are generally lower than those experienced by other models that involve purchase of intangible assets or "goodwill." In addition, physicians tend to voluntarily join foundations more than other models, often because of the physicians' belief in the charitable purposes of the foundation.

The nonprofit and charitable orientation of foundations leads to a general perception that they are less entrepreneurial in nature than other models, and, in some respects, less capable of motivating physicians. Stringent IRS requirements for achieving and maintaining tax-exempt status can also render the formation of foundations expensive and time-consuming. Overall, foundations generate less revenue than other models—often because they provide higher levels of charity care. In some cases, the foundation's partner hospital or health system provides financial support to compensate for inferior financial performance.

The foundation model also has the potential for physician infighting, particularly in foundations that depend heavily on specialists but have business objectives that focus on building primary care delivery systems (Clapp and Jamieson 1997, 21–23). This model also depends on tight integration and works best among physicians willing to sacrifice some individual needs in return for better cost control and access to managed care contracts (Clapp and Jamieson 1997, 21–23).

IPAs: VIEWS FROM THE INDUSTRY

IPAs have suffered greatly from the fact that primary care doctors and specialists have not been able to work out their differences. So it becomes a question of whether specialty IPAs or just primary care IPAs make sense. The problem is that from the medical community's perspective, it really dilutes their influence with re-gard to interaction with payors. From the individual practitioner's point-of-view, they are not getting enough bang out of their repre-sentation.

    —Stuart P. Brogadir, M.D., M.B.A., System Strategist
    Elliot Health System, Manchester, New Hampshire

INDEPENDENT PRACTICE ASSOCIATIONS

Independent practice associations (IPAs) are organized groups of physicians who maintain separate and often solo practices but jointly contract with purchasers on a fee-for-service or capitated basis. Most IPAs have been organized as nonprofit corporations or professional associations or corporations, but some are struc-tured as business corporations (Brasher 1999).

IPAs were developed as a means for physicians outside of groups to participate in managed care contracting yet maintain their independent practices. IPAs affiliated with hospitals have generally featured low risk and low exclusivity and serve as loosely coupled physician-hospital relationships (Dynan, Bazzoli, and Burns 1998, 245). Medical staff-organized IPAs, because of their risk assumption, function as hospital-based HMOs with member-ship restricted to members of the medical staff.

IPAs are generally easier to organize and less costly to man-age than most of the other physician–health system models cur-rently in place, and they give participants a sense of belonging to a larger (physician-only) entity; however, most IPAs are too small to have much leverage with payors. And they will remain small to avoid antitrust challenges because of potential excessive market influence or control. Historically, IPAs have also been hindered by inadequate information systems capabilities that fail to help providers monitor and manage utilization and associated costs of services. With their inadequate capitalization and limited ability to garner contracts, IPAs have had little influence in most markets.

STAFF MODELS

Physicians who participate in staff models are the direct employees of the acquiring entity, which is usually a managed care organization. Physicians sign employment contracts, earn a negotiated salary (sometimes with a performance bonus), and work on a negotiated schedule (Brasher 1999).

This model can be attractive to new physicians who have not built busy, established practices and may not have the entrepreneurial drive to do so, and among physicians with a strong interest in clinical care rather than management. Physicians who have built successful practices but are now interested in winding down by working fewer hours and transitioning their practice to other physicians are also good candidates for this model. Poor candidates for the staff model are physicians who have entrepreneurial spirit and drive and have built successful, economically viable practices.

The problem plaguing the staff model is the challenge of sustaining high enough levels of productivity among the physician groups who are most likely to be willing to participate in this model. The employer in the staff model has direct control over physicians, but physician productivity can decline if productivity and incentive compensation plans are not in place.

STAFF MODEL: VIEW FROM THE INDUSTRY

I think the staff model HMO is going to be much more attractive
and workable for the next generation of physicians who put lifestyle
considerations over income and who do not demand hands-on, self-
directed linkages to patients. It's a difficult model for physicians in
their mid-thirties and above to adjust to. On the other hand, it is a
lot easier to move ahead with a group of physicians who are uni-
fied. So in terms of interactions with managed care payors, the staff
model has a lot of economic advantages.
    —Stuart P. Brogadir, M.D., M.B.A., System Strategist
    Elliot Health System, Manchester, New Hampshire

PHYSICIAN PRACTICE MANAGEMENT COMPANIES

For-profit physician practice management companies (PPMCs)
have emerged as one of the more controversial options for physicians seeking management assistance. About 8 percent of the
nation's 527,000 practicing physicians are affiliated with a PPMC
(Benedict and Feorene 1998). PPMCs attract physicians with
sophisticated management systems and infrastructure and provide tempting access to capital all within a structure in which
physicians have a personal stake via equity in the PPMC. Physicians are also attracted by the potential benefits of market leverage and economies of scale that PPMCs claim to capture, and
some PPMCs offer stock in their companies to physicians.

PPMCs carry inherent risks; both the PPMC and Wall Street
investors expect high returns, sometimes within the range of 25
percent (Benedict and Feorene 1998). Most of the returns come
from physicians' future revenue streams, thus physicians are pres-
sured to sustain this high level of returns over an extended period of time. Many physician-PPMC employment contracts are

for 30 to 40 years. This situation motivates many physicians to pull ancillary services out of hospitals and into practices. As a result, most hospital-PPMC relationships are strained. PPMCs that miss revenue targets or suffer from mismanagement may find themselves in dire straits and unable to continue to access capital that was readily available early in the partnership.

A PPMC's relationship with aligned physicians appears to offer physicians a share in local governance, allowing physicians to retain control over medical decision making and physician recruitment; however, a PPMC is ultimately responsible to its parent company, whose mission is to create financially successful Wall Street investments. The inherent necessity to focus on financials, specifically on revenue growth and incremental earnings, may lead PPMCs to be at odds with physician goals and objectives. Physicians affiliated with PPMCs may find themselves unable to spend resources on patient education, preventive care, practice guidelines, and critical paths—approaches to patient care that take time to develop and implement and may not be capable of proving their direct financial worth over the short term.

Some PPMCs are able to deliver what physician practices alone cannot achieve and what hospitals and physicians together have not accomplished: management expertise, economies of scale, access to capital, and linkages to a large regional or national entity for market clout. But the practice benefits do not necessarily translate into acceptable returns that are demanded by investors.

Given the risky nature of some PPMC affiliations, physicians would do well to reevaluate their relationships with local hospitals to determine if many of the same benefits offered by PPMCs can be negotiated with local healthcare providers whose mission is to meet the healthcare needs of local communities, not Wall Street investors. Many industry watchers now also agree that there are probably very few areas within physician practices where large PPMCs can find enough waste or mismanagement to generate a level of return to satisfy investors.

Although physicians are more wary of PPMCs following the demise of several public and private PPMCs in 1998, PPMCs continue to evolve, and some ventures now focus exclusively and successfully on specialty niches such as emergency services, cardiology, and oncology.

Some of the next generation physician–health system partnership models discussed in the next chapter mimic the goals and expectations of the PPMC–physician practice relationship.

CONCLUSION

The wide variety of physician-hospital affiliation strategies launched during the 1990s reveals the highly experimental nature of these early models of physician-hospital partnerships. The uncertainty about which models have the greatest potential for success is further illustrated in a recent survey of integrated delivery systems conducted by *Modern Healthcare* and Arista Associates, a healthcare consulting firm (Bellandi 1998).

Of the 61 chief executives of multihospital systems who were surveyed, 57 percent said that aligning physicians was the most difficult task they face when building integrated delivery systems, and 77 percent strongly agree that physician integration is central to system success. But the survey showed little consensus on approaches for achieving integration.

The most frequently used models were MSOs (84 percent), direct physician employment (72 percent), and open PHOs (67 percent). Physician employment received the most votes (29 percent) as the most effective model, but 57 percent of the surveyed executives indicated that it is the least profitable model. On the other hand, open PHOs were most frequently cited (21 percent) as the most profitable form of integration, but 27 percent of survey respondents said that open PHOS were the least effective integration model.

Given the prevailing uncertainty about which approaches have the greatest potential for success under what circumstances and the fact that the most prevalent physician-hospital integration models are viewed to be ineffective, the time is right for many hospitals and health systems to review their current physician affiliations and explore the next generation of physician–health system partnerships.

REFERENCES

The Advisory Board Company. 1993. *The Grand Alliance: Vertical Integration Strategies for Physicians and Health Systems.* Washington, D.C.: The Advisory Board Co.

Barnett, A. E. 1998. "Public Physician Practice Management Companies," *Medical Group Management Association Journal* (May/ June): 46.

Bellandi, D. 1998. "Searching for Better Bait." *Modern Healthcare* (October 5): 28.

Benedict, G., and B. Feorene. 1998. "The Not-for-Profit Alternative to PPMCs." *Medical Group Management Association Journal* (May/ June): 39.

Brasher, P. 1999. "New Healthcare Organizations: Physician-Hospital Realignment and Restructuring in the Delivery System." The Advanced Medical Malpractice Course, State Bar of Texas and State Bar of New Mexico. [Online resource. Creation 3/16/95; retrieval 10/ 14/99]. *www.texasbarcle.com.*

Clapp, M., and P. Jamieson. 1997. "Physician Integration Alternatives: Management Services Organizations." *Oncology Issues* 11 (6): 21–23.

Dunevitz, B. 1998. "Survey Report: MSOs Losing Cash, But Optimism Not Dashed." *MGMA Update* 37 (22): 1, 5.

Dynan, L., G. J. Bazzoli, and L. R. Burns. 1998. "Assessing the Extent of Integration Achieved through Physician-Hospital Arrangements." *Journal of Healthcare Management* 43 (3): 245.

"Hospitals that Gobbled Up Physician Practices Feel Ill." 1997. *Wall Street Journal* June 17: B4 (W), B4 (E).

Medical Group Management Association. 1999. [Online resource. Retrieval 9/99]. *www.mgma.org.*

Medimetrix . 1999. [Online article. Retrieval 8/13/99]. *www.mx.com.*

Terry, K. 1998. "Now Hospitals Want to be Your Partner, Not Your Boss." *Medical Economics* (August 24): 81.

Next-Generation Models of
Physician–Health System
Partnerships

THERE IS NO silver bullet for physician–health system partnerships. The inherent complexities of physician-hospital relationships, the historic independence of physicians, and the phe-
nomenal growth and turbulence occurring in the healthcare
delivery system rule out easy answers. But given the flat-out failure or marginal success at best of models that are positioned
between independence and full integration (i.e., acquisition),
health systems and physicians should consider reexploring a
middle ground to see if their needs can be met through a new
generation of alliances.

What will those needs be in the next millennium? Health
systems and physicians bring vastly different expectations to
the bargaining table; therefore, both sides must improve their
understanding of each other to build stronger foundations for
future successful and sustainable partnerships that provide lasting value for both parties.

PHYSICIAN NEEDS AND EXPECTATIONS

A study by Cockley et al. (1995) based on a review of literature and phone interviews with healthcare executives, physician leaders, and consultants, concluded that physicians seek alignment with integrated delivery organizations for the following reasons:

- To align their interests with those of the organization (common vision, shared values, trust, supportive economic incentives);
- To gain the expertise and resources of the partner organization (managed care expertise, ability to reduce administrative burdens of the practice, access to capital and information systems);
- To achieve a degree of security (economic security, income stability, lifestyle issues, benefits);
- To build a buffer against external threats (ally in facing managed care, increasing competition, and legislative and regulatory constraints);
- To maintain autonomy in clinical decision making (authority for decisions affecting clinical practice and patient care);
- To assert physician leadership (meaningful roles in management of the integrating system, bringing clinical perspective to decision making, building a bridge to the larger physician community);
- To become involved in governance (opportunities to shape strategic direction and priorities); and
- To influence the mix of providers (involvement in decision making about the number, mix, and distribution of primary care and specialty physicians and the professional and economic ties between them).

These rationales for seeking alignment suggest that physicians are looking to cooperate and contribute to integrated delivery organizations, but want to retain control over many dimensions of their practice (Cockley et al. 1995).

Physicians' general perspectives and needs were summarized above; however, hospitals and health systems must also keep in mind that physicians are not a homogeneous group but represent a spectrum of highly individualistic professionals who view integration from a wide range of perspectives. Expectations and goals among physicians vary, and the level of autonomy that a physician will relinquish and the amount of risk that a physician is willing to assume to strike a partnership deal will vary. While the formation of larger physician group practices is becoming more common, most self-employed physicians are still members of small practices. According to data from the AMA, in 1997 54.2 percent of self-employed physicians were in groups with two to four physicians and 28.9 percent were in groups with five to nine physicians (Center for Health Policy Research 1998).

A survey conducted by the Center for Health Management Research (CHMR) of nearly 2,000 physicians explored physician attitudes and perceptions toward alignment with their respective organizations (Zuckerman et al. 1998). The results suggest that there are differences by degree of economic alignment, primary care physicians versus specialists, gender, and age group.

In general, integrated (versus nonintegrated) physicians report (Zuckerman et al. 1998):

- Higher levels of trust in the organization with which they are aligned;
- More physician involvement in decision making;
- Greater willingness to invest in network development;
- A preference for group practice;
- A lower anxiety over practice costs; and

• A perception that they have greater clinical autonomy and less desire for control and independence.

These findings are most pronounced among the most integrated physicians (i.e., salaried physicians). The integrated physician responses regarding clinical autonomy are particularly notable, given the widely held view that the least integrated structures give physicians the most autonomy and that highly integrated models are more restrictive (Zuckerman et al. 1998).

The CHMR study also revealed that primary care physicians report that they are less willing to invest time in network development and see fewer signs of clinical integration and cooperation and physician initiatives in controlling quality and cost when compared to specialists. Female physicians reported higher trust levels, perceive greater clinical autonomy, have less anxiety over practice costs, prefer group practices, and have a lower desire for control or independence than male physicians. But females also report less willingness to invest time in network development than males. In terms of age, younger physicians (30 to 39 years of age) and the oldest physicians (60 plus) report the highest trust levels in the organization with which they are aligned, perceive greater physician involvement in decision making, and see greater medical staff organization unity (Zuckerman et al. 1998).

In general, physicians have been relegated to vulnerable economic positions by the restructuring delivery system. Physicians place great value on maximizing their personal productivity and income and are seeking ways to enhance office visit revenue, hospital visit revenue, and procedure revenue to offset professional fee declines. Hospitals and health systems should be in a unique position to help physicians by enabling them to practice efficiently and effectively at the hospital site and in the office. In many hospitals and health systems, organizations have pursued marketing and contracting support and complex equity and revenue sharing strategies with their physicians and have over-looked the value of the basics: accessible surgery schedules and block time, high-quality emergency room and inpatient cover-age, better patient service, accountable and responsive hospital staff, access to patient records, and skilled nursing staff.

The Health Care Advisory Board's National Physician Survey of over 1,000 physicians in 47 states examines drivers of physician loyalty and levels of physician satisfaction (Health Care Advisory Board 1999). According to the 1998 survey, the four top factors influencing physician facility selection, for both primary care physicians and specialists, were (1) the proximity to office, (2) the competence of nursing staff, (3) the reputation of physicians, and (4) the state-of-the art equipment. Efficiency of the facility was rated number five in importance among specialists and number seven among primary care physicians. Contracting and marketing support was ranked least important among the factors examined (Health Care Advisory Board 1999).

The relative importance of each of these physician needs and expectations is subject to interpretation and debate, but the CHMR physician survey reveals a common element to all the factors listed. The CHMR survey reports that of the 12 elements influencing physician perceptions of alignment, trust—the demonstration of mutual respect between physicians and the organizations with which they are aligned—was the single most important factor (Zuckerman et al. 1998, 19).

Relationships that appear to have developed trust exhibit a spirit of partnership, cooperation, and collaboration and are characterized by a sense that their mutual destinies are inextricably linked. They also show a willingness to share control and power and to work together to face strategic and marketplace issues. In sum, these relationships demonstrate that physicians and the organizations with which they are aligned are more powerful working together than they are working alone (Zuckerman et al. 1998, 17).

HOSPITAL AND HEALTH SYSTEM NEEDS AND
EXPECTATIONS

Hospital and health system needs and expectations for physician relationships have tended to emphasize protecting market
share and capturing enrolled lives, but more recently the focus
has been more basic: how to establish sustainable linkages with
physicians without losing a lot of money.

Surveys of hospital and system CEOs conducted by Alexander
et al. (1996) reveal that organization strategies tend to follow three
themes:

1. Protect existing markets (stop the loss of inpatient mar-
    ket share, prevent practice acquisitions by competitors,
    block the loss of referral sources, keep primary physi-
    cians from moving to competing networks, stop the loss
    of physicians moving into retirement);
2. Expand into new markets (broaden primary care base,
    improve managed care positioning, establish primary
    care networks, position the organization for direct con-
    tracting and "one-stop shopping" for payors); and
3. Integrate and coordinate delivery (vertically integrate
    delivery and insurance functions, achieve scale econo-
    mies through consolidated management systems,
    develop an integrated delivery organization, improve
    quality through coordinated care systems, enhance
    community access to services).

CEOs participating in this survey ranked these three strategies
as having near equal importance, but case study interviews with
these executives distill these concepts. Improving economic alignment with physicians was frequently mentioned during the interviews (Alexander et al. 1996). Given the heavy financial losses
hospitals have suffered through the last generation of physician–

NEXT-GENERATION PARTNERSHIP MODELS:
VIEWS FROM THE INDUSTRY

In the future you are going to start to see the formation of smaller groups, not 50- or 60-person groups, but four- to eight-person groups. I think you are going to see hospital closings in the next five years. I wouldn't be surprised if you see between 10 to 15 hospitals close in New Jersey. There will be some equilibrium in the markets, so that providers can begin to have some leverage with the third parties. And when that happens, then there may be a potential moment in time where if people are smart, they can create organizations that will have legs for the future.
   —Adam Henick, Executive Director
      Montefiore Medical Group, New York, New York

The only thing that is helping our physicians to listen and be sympathetic and actually work with us is the fact that the numbers don't lie. When our hospital's bottom line is flat and we have a major subsidy going on in a physician organization, it doesn't take a rocket scientist to figure out that we can continue this for "x" amount of time, and then the system will be bankrupt. If that happens, physicians will be on the losing end too, and they will be looking for employment under very adverse situations. If we work together now, it is going to be painful, but we can potentially salvage the long-term benefits of these relationships if we just take some short-term pain and that means giving up some of the artificial economic environment that healthcare systems have created.
   —Christopher Howard, Executive Vice President
      Health*first* Inc., Oklahoma City, Oklahoma

health system partnerships and the failed execution of partnership models, it is not surprising that economic alignment is a popular theme. Hospital and health system executives seem to be interested in sharing risk and reward and losing the often ill-placed image of having "deep pockets" when it comes to the ability to sustain the long-term financial losses associated with many of the previously created partnership models.

GUIDING PRINCIPLES FOR NEXT GENERATION PHYSICIAN–HEALTH SYSTEM PARTNERSHIPS

Given the divergent needs and expectations of physicians, hospitals, and health systems, how do these groups move forward to forge sustainable, economically viable relationships that will address the strategic issues and market realities of the next century? A number of guiding principles emerge that account for the needs and expectations of both physicians and healthcare organizations.

Offer physicians choice. Although physicians have common interests and goals, the "one size fits all" approach will not work. Hospitals and health systems should offer an array of alternative relationships to fit the interests and comfort levels of both specialists and primary care physicians. These relationships may range from loose integration to tight integration (see Figure 3-1). The physician's trust in a credible and high-quality hospital and its medical staff determines, to a great extent, whether a meaningful partnership can be created at the outset. It is important to note, however, that research does not support the notion that physician–health system alliances must pass through lower levels of integration before evolving to more tightly aligned relationships (Zuckerman et al. 1998, 11). Some physicians may be prepared to skip intermediate stages of integrated relationships and move to more fully integrated partnerships such as joint ventures or full-risk contracting. Some physicians may need to take a more cautious approach. Research does indicate that hospitals that offer both tight and loose levels of integrated relationships are more successful in achieving higher levels of overall integration than those organizations where loose only or tight only alliances are implemented (Dynan, Bazzoli, and Burns 1998).

FIGURE 3.1 Range of Potential Physician–Health System Partnership Examples

INDEPENDENT PHYSICIANS	LOOSE INTEGRATION	MODERATE INTEGRATION	TIGHT INTEGRATION

• Physician practice liaison
• Recruitment assistance
• Lounge, cafeteria, parking
• Lab courier
	• Information systems linkages (laboratory information system, radiology information system, hospital information system)
	• Limited practice management services
	  • Answering service
	  • Transcription
	  • Supplies purchasing
	  • Practice promotion
	• Joint program development (e.g., medical directors)
	• PHO
	• Joint contract participation
		• Recruitment and start-up practice growth loans
		• Comprehensive practice management services
		• Blunder management services
		  • Staffing
		  • Billing/ collections
		  • Facility leasing
		• Global contracting
		• Joint operating agreements
			• Acquisition and employment
			• Employment
			• Joint ventures (ambulatory surgery center, ambulatory care center, medical office building, program development)
			• Full-risk contracting or contracting exclusivity

PARTNERSHIP STRATEGIES

Physician manpower deficits / 15 percent managed care penetration / "Polite" hospital system competition	Physician surpluses / 50 percent + managed care penetration / "Fierce" hospital system competition

• Physician manpower deficits
• 15 percent managed care penetration
• "Polite" hospital system competition

• Physician surpluses
• 50 percent + managed care penetration
• "Fierce" hospital system competition

FIT WITH MARKETS WITH…

Build partnerships that add value. Given the volatile nature of healthcare reimbursement and projections of imminent hospital closures, hospitals, health systems, and physicians must focus on income enhancement and strengthening economic and market viability. Collaborations must add demonstrated value for all partners, not just rest on a foundation of "everyone else is trying this approach, so we should too." Only "value-added" partnerships will solidify full commitment to the partnership rather than creating easily unwound, superficial relationships. Value for physicians means increased access to incremental contracts and hospitals fostering practice viability and assisting with practice efficiency. The financial benefits of this assistance should be tangibly demonstrated by evaluating prepartnership and postpartnership income statements. For hospitals, value boils down to not losing money, maintaining or improving levels of market share, and improving managed care contracting positions.

Choose participants wisely. All prospective partners in the alliance must be scrutinized for the strengths and weaknesses they bring to the relationship, the potential role they will fulfill, and the expected returns from the relationship. The "more is better" theory for participants is not a harbinger of success. Selectivity before the partnership is finalized will ensure fewer strained relationships and improve prospects for less volatile collaborations than have occurred in the past. If specific criteria for participation are not established at the outset, excluding physicians who wish to participate will be very difficult. These criteria must include specific performance requirements and data must be available at the individual level to objectively screen out poor performers either before or after the partnership model is implemented.

Identify leaders with the vision, rapport, and skill to build and nurture the partnership. These leaders may serve in the roles of a "boundary spanner" or "champion" who circulates among the partners, clarifies issues and builds consensus, and generally energizes and invigorates the collaborative relationship (Zuckerman et al. 1998, 27). In particular, hospitals and health systems may need to aggressively seek out and mentor physician leaders and provide the means for these individuals to receive the education and support needed to nurture their leadership skills. These physician leaders must then be given the opportunity to be actively involved in clinical decision making as well as organizational policy and strategy development, and must not just serve in figurehead positions that give a false appearance of involvement. Fostering substantial input and leadership for physicians in new partnership models will help avoid one of the most common mistakes of previous models: imbalance of power.

Establish a game plan with definitive rules. All participants in the relationship must fully understand the goals and objectives of the partnership and the potential risks and rewards that may be encountered if the relationship unfolds. Everyone should also understand the potential exit triggers, strategies, and consequences. The same plan for the partnerships should be built for the long term, rather than focusing only on short-term efforts.

Keep relationships flexible. Physician–health system relationships should be flexible enough to adapt, when appropriate, to changes within the organization and in the healthcare delivery environment. Examples include allowing the partners to pursue new strategic initiatives or develop reconfigured practices to take advantage of specific opportunities.

Divest of unproductive, financially draining, long-term relationships. Healthcare systems and physicians have some difficult choices ahead. Although strategies for stemming financial losses and improving the productivity of employed physicians exist, some relationships may need to be restructured or terminated if the system is to remain viable. A case study describing the restructuring process is included in chapter 5 of this book.

Ensure that physician–health system relationships are incentive based. Compensation systems for physicians must link performance to compensation and provide tangible evidence of the risks and rewards of physician performance. Compensation systems must also provide equitable treatment of primary care physicians and specialists to ensure that neither group is being penalized for performance that has a desirable effect on patient care and the system's financial performance. Further information on incentive compensation approaches and methodologies is included in chapter 8 of this book.

Offer high-quality hospital and medical staff services. No amount of incentives or marketing and contracting support can compensate for a hospital whose patient care and medical staff services are subpar. Hospitals and health systems must ensure that their houses are in order before they campaign to convince physicians of their value as a partner with admirable healthcare delivery expertise. High-quality hospitals and medical staffs attract high-quality physician practices.

Agree on performance standards and measurement. Mutually agreed-on expectations for the partnership including utilization management protocols and provider performance assessment tools ensure that all participants in the partnership understand the parameters of the relationship. Guidelines should exist for educating and potentially disciplining or excluding physicians who fail to meet quality standards and consistently exceed guidelines for treatment costs. Performance should be monitored and shared with physician practices on a regular basis (see chapter 5 for additional information). Similarly, the performance of hospital operations and systems needs to be regularly measured, monitored, and reported. Examples include the return on investment for a joint venture ambulatory surgery center or the collection rate and days in accounts receivable for physician accounts that are the responsibility of the hospital.

Use acquisition as a strategy of last resort. Except in limited cases, practice acquisition should be avoided in favor of more creative partnerships that draw upon the strengths of each partner and protect each from further financial losses.

Perhaps the most important issue to keep in mind as hospitals, health systems, and physicians reevaluate their future relationships is that how partnerships are built and the environment in which they are created are as important as the resulting partnership structures. The process of forging new alliances and the quality of the relationships that emerge from that process provide rare opportunities for hospitals to earn and retain physician trust—trust that may have been damaged or lost in the previous wave of partnership efforts.

Several indicators of trust-based relationships between physicians and healthcare organizations exist (Zuckerman et al. 1998).

- Informal and formal open and frequent communication, including opportunities to become familiar and comfortable with one another and to work through issues together in a variety of settings and contexts;
- Willingness to share data so that full information is available to all parties and so that parties are motivated and invested in working toward common goals; and
- Evidence of successful collaborations and demonstrations of how working together has resulted in "small victories" as desired outcomes are pursued.

Most importantly, trust is earned by participants who "walk the talk"—meet commitments, keep their word, do what they say they will do, and demonstrate great respect for the other party's competencies and opinions.

NEXT-GENERATION MODELS FOR PHYSICIAN–HEALTH SYSTEM PARTNERSHIPS

The next phase of physician–health system partnerships must build on the successes of their predecessors and address the shortcomings in structure and management that have plagued the disintegrating models discussed in chapter 2. Local hospitals and health systems, with their commitment to community health and role as known commodities, are in favorable positions to use next-generation models to forge stronger ties with physicians.

This chapter presents potential models for hospitals, health systems, and physicians to consider as they evaluate how to proceed into the next millennium of healthcare. These example models exhibit the transition of theory into practice as they begin to show evidence of demonstrating the guiding principles of physician–health system partnerships discussed earlier in this chapter. Ten models and numerous examples of these models are presented in this chapter.

MODEL #1: ECONOMIC INTEGRATION

As discussed in the opening sections of this chapter, both physicians and hospital executives agree that economic alignment is a critical component of successful physician-hospital relationships. In many cases, the economic incentives that used to exist in physician practices were substantially reduced when physicians became wholly integrated with health systems and MSOs. The absence of incentives has resulted in financial disaster in some cases. For some organizations, the next step is to divest of existing physician relationships and create new ones with more aligned economic and strategic incentives. The litmus test for this model is its ability to substantiate economic value for physicians through maintenance or improvement of practice income and for the hospital partner through maintenance or improvement in the hospital's financial positioning.

Below are examples of economic integration currently in practice. For the purposes of this book, an economic model of physician-hospital partnerships is a structure that creates some shared financial risk and reward between and among hospital and physician participants. The degree of shared risk and reward can be extensive or limited, depending on the depth of the partnership, but is commensurate with the level of investment and commitment. The key element is interdependent financial performance.

Joint Operating Agreements

Joint operating agreements (JOAs) are an economic alignment strategy becoming more prevalent as a means to partner with physicians. Joint operating agreements secure physician participation in clinical, operational, or other initiatives by formally dividing responsibility for these initiatives between hospital and physician representatives. The number of physicians participating in the agreement can vary, depending on the nature and extent of the partnership. For example, one or two physicians could form a JOA with a hospital to collaboratively recruit additional physicians, or an entire department of the medical staff could form a JOA with the hospital to develop a hospital's service line (e.g., cardiology or oncology services).

Drawing increased interest since the July 1999 ban on gainsharing took effect, joint operating agreements borrow the most attractive aspect of gainsharing—alignment of hospital and physician clinical and operational incentives—but leave behind the Achilles heal of gainsharing programs—the risk of fostering a reduction in patient care. Joint operating agreements take a variety of forms, from management or personal services agreements to clinical protocols. The rights, responsibilities, and rewards are spelled out in a document and agreed to by all parties of the agreement. Where physician commitment requires significant expenditure of time or resources, reimbursement of the physician is tied to simple, easy-to-measure and easy-to-document market rates. Joint operating agreements are discussed further in chapter 4.

Guaranteed Lines of Credit

For hospitals and health systems with physician practices that are interested in accessing capital (often those practices comprising entrepreneurial or younger physicians), providing guaranteed lines of credit for physicians may be an attractive option. In such a situation, the hospital or health system serves as a guarantor of a loan to a physician practice, ostensibly for practice growth and development. This approach financially links the hospital or system with physicians and encourages the hospital to be vested in and supportive of the overall success of the practice, while falling short of practice acquisition and its inevitable financially draining aftermath.

Efforts to establish stronger ties with physicians by providing access to capital can backfire in some situations. An adversarial relationship may emerge if payments are not made because of a lack of practice growth and failure to achieve incremental earnings, which may lead to litigation or foreclosure. As with all partnership models, hospitals and health systems must carefully evaluate the assumptions upon which practice growth and development are predicated and determine whether the potential risks of being a lender are offset by the benefits that may be derived from strengthened ties with physicians.

In some situations, hospitals or systems may not be financially capable of providing support. Genesee Hospital in Rochester, New York, has limited ability to provide lines of credit, but has established a creative approach for supporting practices financially. Through partnership agreements, the hospital has set up professional accounts that allow practices to remain private and retain independence and decision-making authority. The professional accounts give the practices access to some of the system's resources for capitalizing the practices and recruiting new physicians; thus the hospital can subsidize new physician

---

FULL-RISK CONTRACTING: VIEWS FROM THE INDUSTRY

In most of the medical communities that I have seen, physicians and hospitals have signed up for full-risk contracts but they don't know what it really costs them to manage care. They have not been able to generate enough internal data to know how they can manage care and they don't have the medical management capabilities to do it. I think full-risk contracting is clearly a way to survive, but I would say that almost no medical communities that I have seen are prepared for it.

    —Stuart P. Brogadir, M.D., M.B.A., System Strategist
    Elliot Health System,
    Manchester, New Hampshire

---

recruitment for a period of time with buy-out provisions over a one-year to three-year period.

Full-Risk Contracting and Contracting Exclusivity

A key factor in physician practice viability is determining which party bears the risk for overuse or underuse of services. Hospitals and health systems have historically assumed financial risk through Medicare DRG payments. Physicians have assumed financial risk through capitation. According to a recent survey of physicians in office-based private practice, 44 percent of physicians in all fields received capitation payments in 1998 (Terry 1999). In an effort to more equitably align economic incentives of participating providers, some hospitals have entered into full- or global-risk contracts with physicians and other providers.

    Hospitals and physicians have generally been wary of full-risk contracting. Physicians may be reluctant to assume risk for utilization that involves potentially inefficient and costly hospital operations and systems. Similarly, hospitals can be hesitant to share risk with physicians when the physician income is directly related to their utilization (i.e., visits, procedures, admissions). For physicians, financial risk assumption means physicians must charge at appropriate levels and control expenses to maintain a financially viable practice. If use increases without clinical risk assumption (i.e., capitation), physicians can increase productivity to increase revenue.

With clinical risk assumption, if use increases, revenue most likely will not increase. Thus, as risk-sharing relationships are forged, one central question is, "at risk for what?" What is the predicted utilization of services for a defined population? What are we at risk for—all services, hospital and physician services? In addition, performance measures and controls must be in place to ensure that the contracting relationship is financially sound.

The number of hospitals and physicians participating in full-risk contracts is rather small. Only 10 percent of all HMO contracts involve full-risk or global contracting agreements (Institute for the Future, 1998).

Full-risk contracting and contracting exclusivity are generally more appropriate for major metropolitan markets with large, hospital-linked multispecialty practices that have the expertise and savvy to measure and manage utilization and performance. These strategies are generally only used for primary care services. Although some providers may elect to participate in full-risk contracting, many experts predict that neither global capitation nor discounted fee-for-service arrangements are sustainable over the long term.

Right of First Refusal Contracts

As an alternative to the largely flawed strategy of practice acquisition, some hospitals and health systems have extended right of first refusal contracts to selected physicians. If at any time

RIGHT OF FIRST REFUSAL: VIEWS FROM THE INDUSTRY

I think right of first refusal contracts are important because they convey that physicians and hospitals really want to partner and that they need to come to one another primarily to make decisions. But it also says that sometimes they won't agree or sometimes it won't be a beneficial arrangement for both sides. It basically gives them the sense that they can agree to disagree, but they still have to treat each other as their primary partner.

  —Stuart P. Brogadir, M.D., M.B.A., System Strategist
  Elliot Health System
  Manchester, New Hampshire

during the contract period (typically three to five years), the physicians consider selling their practice, the hospital or health system is given the first opportunity to purchase the practice. In return for the right of first refusal contract, participating physicians receive a cash payment. These payments may be in the $10,000 to $30,000 range for the term of the contract. As part of the contract, physicians often agree to exclusive participation in managed care contracts negotiated by the hospital or system and sign a noncompete agreement stating that the physicians will not set up ambulatory care services to compete with the hospital.

This model seems particularly applicable to ultracompetitive markets where major systems, in an effort to buy market share, are continuing to acquire physician practices. This strategy puts a hospital in a position to purchase a practice if and only if a competitor continues to acquire practices. Right of first refusal contracts are often not executed, but they do raise the comfort level of hospitals that then are confident that their physician base is secure; physicians gain some comfort that their practices have value in their linkage to a health system.

MODEL #2: REAL ESTATE PARTNERSHIPS

Having geographically dispersed ambulatory care facilities as well as medical office buildings in close proximity to hospital campuses have become key attributes for hospitals and systems. Providers want to provide a wide area of patient populations with convenient access to physicians and facilities. Meanwhile, physicians who tend to be more inpatient or operating room based place high value on having office space that allows short and convenient commutes to a hospital facility. Other physicians may prefer to have key services provided at a satellite facility rather than the hospital facility because of ease of access and convenience.

A natural outgrowth of these facility needs is for hospitals and physicians to pursue joint real estate partnerships in an effort to establish long-term commitments to each other. The legal and financial structures of ownership and management of a medical office building or ambulatory care center can vary, depending on the needs and interests of the hospital and participating physicians. Numerous ownership and participation options are available for partnerships between a hospital, physician practices, and real estate developers who want to own facilities. Hospitals and physicians have developed various arrangements for office space, ambulatory surgery centers, and ambulatory services through joint ventures, management services agreements, and other structures. In some cases, hospitals have colocated convenient and accessible ambulatory services (e.g., imaging, phlebotomy, cardiac diagnostic services) with practices of four or more physicians.

Another example of a facility partnership is a wellness center. These facilities enable primary care physicians and occasionally some specialists to colocate with complementary, hospital-sponsored diagnostic and treatment services such as women's health, imaging, sports medicine, physical therapy, and laboratory

REAL ESTATE PARTNERSHIPS: VIEWS FROM THE INDUSTRY

We feel that our ability to access capital to geographically expand access to our services and to our physicians is going to occur through partnerships with our physicians who are willing to invest. In particular, we are looking at potential joint venture arrangements with our physicians, particularly in the area of ambulatory surgery.

> —Paul Kempinski, Vice President
> Ambulatory Services, The Genesee Hospital
> Rochester, New York

Because proximity still is high on the list of physician desires and they are looking more and more at alternative investment methodologies to prop up their future, some real estate ventures are viable for the purpose of aligning physicians to healthcare systems. But the incentives on both sides must be aligned. In the past, it would not be unusual for a hospital or healthcare system to enter a joint venture with a physician on a piece of real estate just for the purpose of tightening the relationship with that doctor. Now we are finding more and more that systems will only enter into the real estate venture if the investment itself can be prosperous in addition to building a relationship with the physician. There aren't any more free rides—or there are fewer and fewer free rides.

> —Christopher Howard, Executive Vice President
> Health*first* Inc., Oklahoma City, Oklahoma

The economic future of hospitals and physicians are the same—outpatient care. I think partnerships to develop outpatient care facilities can be beneficial and enable both parties to move ahead together. It's a very healthy way for physicians and hospitals who have traditionally been sort of natural enemies to move ahead and cooperate in the future

> —Stuart P. Brogadir, M.D., M.B.A., System Strategist
> Elliot Health System, Manchester, New Hampshire

services. Retail components may include services such as a pharmacy, health food store, restaurant, optical shop, and durable medical equipment store.

Transylvania Community Hospital in Brevard, North Carolina, has successfully put the real estate partnership model in place on its hospital campus. This 94-bed community hospital, including 40 chemical dependency beds, currently has five buildings developed through partnerships with its physicians. About half of the hospital's active medical staff is located in these buildings, and both specialists and primary care physicians participate in the facility partnerships.

The hospital's for-profit subsidiary, Transylvania Services, Inc. (TSI), serves as the general partner while the physicians are limited partners. The land for the buildings, located on the hospital campus, was deeded to TSI; TSI then extends long-term leases on the land to the partners. The physicians build equity in their facilities without laying out the capital that would be required if they had purchased and developed the property on their own. Location—proximity to other physicians and to the hospital—is also an advantage. Physicians in these buildings have direct access to the hospital's computer system rather than access through modems or more costly linkages.

Having physicians in close proximity has enhanced the hospital's image as a destination for healthcare services. Logistical advantages such as accessibility for formal and informal visits by hospital staff are also enjoyed. Meetings can be held in physician offices rather than always requiring physicians to travel to the hospital. Overall, proximity has enabled Transylvania to continue its commitment to including physicians in key operational projects such as quality improvement, clinical pathways, and other areas of mutual interest to physicians and the hospital. Recruitment of physicians has also been enhanced by the availability of office space in a region where local developers are not constructing professional office space.

Transylvania Community Hospital recognizes that keeping physicians on campus is not an end-all strategy and is considering options for extending primary care through its service area. The hospital has also recognized the need for flexibility in facility partnerships to meet the needs of hospital-owned physicians and others. According to Mark Emory, director of professional/support services at Transylvania Community Hospital,

> Having physicians on campus ties them more to what we are doing here and has the community looking at the hospital campus as a central location for healthcare. We're trying to develop a gateway approach to healthcare in terms of a vision for us and how we want our market to look at us. We can't provide everything here at a small hospital, but we are the place to start.

MODEL #3: JOINT PROGRAM DEVELOPMENT
PARTNERSHIPS

Program development partnerships are not a new model of physician–health system partnerships. These alliances have existed for years between hospitals and their more entrepreneurial physicians, with the goal of building successful programs that benefit physicians, hospitals, and patients by providing a higher level of service while garnering more market share and volume and increasing the number of patients served. Many of these program initiatives focus on ambulatory services such as women's health, surgery, oncology, and cardiology. Some are structured as legal joint ventures.

Historically, many joint program development models failed for several reasons. Hospitals frequently assumed all of the risk for the ventures and often contributed the majority of funding for the programs with the physicians' blessings. This approach solidified hospitals' identities as the dominant partners and left

JOINT PROGRAM DEVELOPMENT: VIEWS FROM THE INDUSTRY

If legal restrictions don't prevent it, joint program development can start moving hospitals and physicians into more integrated relationships. You are pooling capital and working together on delivering a service rather than just providing a functional component of that service. But you have to give consideration to the longevity of the project and the ability to unwind the deal when it is no longer desirable.
—D. Louis Glaser, Esq., Partner
Gardner, Carton & Douglas, Chicago, Illinois

Joint program development speaks for itself. It's an acknowledgment that hospitals aren't totally in charge of healthcare and some prepackaged programs aren't really packaged medically appropriately. On the other hand, physicians are traditionally not that astute in terms of the expense and marketing of programs, so doing programs together with the appropriate medical and financial expertise can be a successful partnership.
—Stuart P. Brogadir, M.D., M.B.A., System Strategist
Elliot Health System, Manchester, New Hampshire

physicians in the position of appearing anxious to reap the financial benefits of the partnerships with little associated investment or risk.

One of the most prevalent sources of physician dissatisfaction with joint ventures has been the inferior return on investment performance. For example, incremental practice income derived from improved productivity in a freestanding ambulatory surgery center (e.g., performing six cases per day compared to four per day in the hospital) usually far exceeds the return on capital investment in a joint venture relationship.

As many of the joint program ventures have started to unbundle, a new generation of joint program arrangements has emerged. These new partnerships are structured to ensure that the level of risk and reward are commensurate with the level of investment.

The newer models of joint program development do not necessarily conform to a true joint venture relationship. The alliance may start as a medical director relationship for a program or simply a congenial agreement to work together to develop a program that will benefit both groups and potentially build a foundation for a more formal venture partnership in the future. Physician and hospital participants are generally more committed to the venture if each perceives a tangible strategic or economic benefit, and substantial commitment (time and capital) is required as a condition of the joint venture.

As these program partnerships are being built, hospitals and health systems should keep in mind that physicians will have a different level of commitment to the project. Physicians are usually using personal funds to invest in the program and spending valuable time away from revenue-producing activities when they participate in joint program discussions. Meanwhile, hospital staff are paid to spend time in meetings and are more removed financially because they are appropriating hospital funds. A program that offers a scope of services and a particular relationship to the economic benefit of the physician practices creates necessary incentives to encourage physician participation.

Physicians comment on the tendency of many hospitals to fight outmigration of their "low-tech" ambulatory services, even those services for which outmigration to a physician practice would be considered inevitable, such as chemotherapy, minor procedures, and simple diagnostic tests and procedures. A hospital in the Northeast is a good example of how some hospitals' unwillingness to jointly work with physicians to develop ambulatory services often results in devastating losses.

About six years ago, a group of six physicians approached the hospital about developing an ambulatory surgery center that would potentially improve both the hospital's and physicians' productivity, performance, and managed care positioning. The hospital made it clear that they wanted to keep all ambulatory surgery volume within their facility and extended no overtures to support the physicians. The physicians proceeded to obtain loans and developed the facility independently, with great success. The hospital proceeded to damage their credibility further by holding payors "hostage" by virtue of their "discounted" inpatient rates. The hospital insisted that a condition of the discounted rate was that payors had to agree to use outpatient services at the hospital and not at the physician-owned ambulatory surgery center.

The hospital then failed once again by becoming intransigent about participating in any venture that they did not own and run. When other area surgeons became concerned that the hospital's endoscopy services were too expensive and placed the physicians and hospital at a disadvantage for managed care contracting, they approached the hospital about developing a dedicated facility for endoscopy. The hospital declined to become involved, so the surgeons joined the physician-owned ambulatory surgery center. Endoscopy procedures are now performed at the center for about 25 to 30 percent of the hospital charges and generate an admirable profit for the physicians.

Thoughtful and insightful hospital leaders will realize that it is better to have 50 percent of service revenue and potentially strong, healthy ties with physicians, than to have no share of the revenue and an alienated medical staff. Outmigration of some ambulatory services is inevitable. The key is to acknowledge this transition of services to other settings and view it as an opportunity to partner with physicians.

MODEL #4: INFORMATION SYSTEM LINKAGES

Joint development of information technology is a largely untapped area for strengthening sustainable linkages between hospitals and health systems and physicians. Access to accurate, timely,

INFORMATION SYSTEMS: VIEWS FROM THE INDUSTRY

Information system development is a very fertile avenue. Physicians are in dramatic need of good information technology. But most healthcare systems don't have the expertise to get this technology to the physicians and they don't understand what physicians need. So hospitals have jumped into implementing information systems and done a botched job of it, further antagonizing the physicians. If you want to see the hell and fury of a physician, just go and screw up their practice.

—Adam Henick, Executive Director
Montefiore Medical Group
New York, New York

and integrated clinical and financial data will be the hallmark of successful providers who must track physician, hospital, and other provider outcomes; provide accurate and current patient information that can be accessed at multiple sites; monitor productivity and incentive programs; and handle scheduling for an increasing number of ambulatory sites. Particularly crucial for physicians and hospitals participating in risk contracts is the ability to follow electronically based care, case, and disease management protocols to more efficiently care for and track the health status of a population.

Information system linkages can significantly benefit physician practices as they offer physicians the opportunity to integrate with a hospital or health system. Such integration may include linkages to laboratory information systems, imaging reports, patient information, and scheduling.

Hospitals and health systems must take the lead in developing these hospital and laboratory information systems; however, physicians, as the most important end users, must participate as partners in developing information technology systems that enhance their medical practices rather than add extra hassles to already burdened staff.

This arena has great room for improvement, as software development has lagged woefully behind the rapidly increasing needs of providers. Nevertheless hospitals and physicians must work with available resources to weave together information system components that will one day catch up to the demands of the healthcare delivery system.

A number of academic medical centers have been developing web-based information systems to serve as platforms for linkages to physician practices. These systems offer several benefits to physicians. Physician practices can access hospital information systems to obtain test results and patient records and tap into scheduling systems. A list of physician practices may also be included on the hospital or system web site, enabling new patients to find physicians.

The University of Pennsylvania Health System web site (*med.upenn.edu*) gives physicians access to the following resources:

- Penn Health Management: a system with components of preventive, wellness, and disease management initiatives across the entire University of Pennsylvania Health System;
- *Penn Today*: a continuing medical education resource for private practice and faculty physicians;
- Listing of accepted health plans; and
- Information for employers about services such as occupational medicine.

The University of Rochester Medical Center also offers a number of services to physicians through its web site (*stronghealth.rochester.edu*), including:

- Information on each affiliate of Strong Health;
- Linkages to the medical center web site to help promote individual and group practices;
- Health education and continuing medical education materials; and
- Inclusion in the StrongCare Health Plan (managed care product) provider directory.

MODEL #5: EMPLOYMENT WITHOUT ACQUISITION

As practice acquisitions have waned in popularity, employment of physicians without acquisition has become a more common partnership approach. These employment arrangements usually include incentive-laden compensation agreements. Although the drawbacks of employing physicians still exist with this model, the financial burden of practice acquisition has been removed and energies can be focused more directly on the integration of physician services with hospital services.

Under this model, the hospital contracts with a physician to provide services at a lower than traditional base salary, ideally no more than 80 percent of previous base levels, with the contract often specifying a required level of productivity and putting a large portion of the physician's income at risk for productivity and other performance measures. Overall, compensation should be commensurate with the level of productivity (e.g., income production, relative value, or "work" units). This approach may not be welcomed by many physicians because of income reduction; however, it is an opportunity for hospitals and physicians to craft new relationships based on the economic realities of the marketplace and build in performance-based incentives, preferably before the relationship is in financial crisis.

For physicians, an employment relationship helps provide security and can substantially reduce management responsibilities,

---

EMPLOYMENT WITHOUT ACQUISITION: VIEWS FROM THE INDUSTRY

Employment without acquisition helps remove the tension that emerges when a hospital has overpaid for a practice that proves to be an underperforming asset. There are still a lot of issues associated with physician employment and taking someone who has been independent and entrepreneurial and putting them into a more bureaucratic structure. But certainly I think it gives you the opportunity to focus on the right issues by relieving some of the stress and tension associated with the economic burden of buying a practice.

—D. Louis Glaser, Esq., Partner
Gardner, Carton & Douglas, Chicago, Illinois

---

which is why this model is particularly relevant to young physicians who are starting a practice and rarely have assets to acquire. Some employment arrangements may be structured to enhance physician incomes, offering such incentives as signing bonuses or teaching and administrative stipends, provided that the hospital or system can prove that there is genuine, substantive work to be done. Payments are usually made at fair-market value to compensate physicians at a reasonable level.

A caveat of the employment without acquisition approach is its potential for creating divisiveness among the medical community who may view the "favorite" physicians as getting preferential treatment by being offered employment contracts. To avoid this potential land mine, employment without acquisition partnerships must be handled openly, with the legitimate reasons for the relationship demonstrated to be market appropriate.

St. Barnabas Health System in Livingston, New Jersey, uses the employment without acquisition approach to staff inner-city, multispecialty health clinics. The clinic physicians are employees who are on payroll and receive benefits. The system's hospitals bill and collect for the clinic physicians. Most of these employed physicians are full-time employees, although a few are part-time providers with small practices on the side.

Genesee Hospital in Rochester, New York, has adapted the employment without acquisition approach by extending service agreements to physicians for administrative duties. The hospital uses these practices as laboratories to try new methods of practice management and enhancement. In general, the hospital's modus operandi has been to hire physicians as employees (without acquisition) to support a private practice base of physicians, only as a last resort will the hospital consider purchasing a practice.

William Beaumont Hospital in Troy and Royal Oak, Michigan, has put another unique spin on employing physicians. The hospital, which has avoided practice acquisition, has developed an outreach program that includes employment of primary care residents. The hospital has a large primary care residency program, but historically many residents graduated and left the area or moved on to competing hospitals. The hospital was spending significant funds on educating residents, only to have them leave the system. In addition, the hospital recognized that a large portion of its success was derived from its active, private medical staff, and was concerned that new practices were not being formed, particularly in areas of community need.

To respond to these concerns, the hospital developed a mentor program and a transition model in 1995. Under both programs, new physicians are employed for a period of time for the purpose of building their practice to the point of being financially self-supporting. The highest priority practices for inclusion in either program are in geographic areas and specialties deemed underserved by a community-needs analysis. Approximately 30 physicians participate in the programs at any given time. In the transition model, senior "preretirement" physicians transition their practice to a new associate who eventually assumes responsibility for the practice. In the mentor model, new physicians learn to grow and maintain a busy and successful private practice under the tutelage of a senior, private practice physician.

MODEL #6: ACQUISITION WITHOUT EMPLOYMENT

Although practice acquisitions are becoming increasingly rare, when they do occur, some hospitals and systems are moving away from the traditional employment model in favor of an independent contractor approach, similar to the one used by PPMCs. However, hospitals should be aware of the hard lesson that PPMCs have recently learned: there usually are not 15 percent margins on the bottom line of practices to be made by anybody other than physicians. At best, hospitals should expect to break even with their independent contractor physicians and hope that the relationships will prove fruitful in other ways.

In the acquisition without employment relationship, a hospital or system acquires the tangible or intangible (i.e., goodwill) assets of a practice, but the physician does not become an employee. The physician continues to be responsible for income generation and maintenance of reasonable expense levels to generate sufficient income. This strategy has been particularly prevalent among retiring physicians, when hospitals buy practices to obtain access to records, patient lists, and office buildings in strategic locations, and then place new physicians in the practices. The new physician is introduced to the senior physician's patients and, over time, these patients are "transitioned" to the new, younger physician. In the best case scenario, the transition is accomplished within a generous enough time frame so that the replacement physician earns the loyalty of the retiring physician's patients.

ACQUISITION WITHOUT EMPLOYMENT: VIEWS FROM THE INDUSTRY

When facing a situation of acquisition without employment, hospitals need to ask themselves whether or not there is real value in the acquisition or are they better off trying to help another physician to enter the market and compete on their own. Unless you have a unique situation, such as a retiring physician, acquisitions without employment can be elusory—you're not getting what you want.
— D. Louis Glaser, Esq., Partner
Gardner, Carton & Douglas, Chicago, Illinois

MODEL #7: NEXT-GENERATION MSOs

A second generation of MSOs is now emerging that is more committed to providing the specific services physicians truly want and demonstrating that those services can provide value to practices. Many physicians were never convinced that MSOs could save money by cutting costs and providing scale economies. Physicians who bought into the model were often constrained by the package deals that early iterations of MSOs offered and disappointed when the MSOs were unable to deliver on their promises of offering a full spectrum of value-added services for physicians. Often, the MSO billings and collections' performance was inferior to pre-MSO participation levels, and other MSO services such as staffing, recruitment, and information systems did not provide benefits to the practice as promised. Overall, MSO practice management services have rarely provided the same or better levels of service for the costs charged to the practice.

Next-generation MSOs are generally offering services on an à la carte basis or cafeteria-style plan, allowing physicians to choose the specific services that best suit their needs, such as billing and collections, transcription services, arranging on-call

NEXT-GENERATION MSOs: VIEWS FROM THE INDUSTRY

The new models of MSOs are letting physicians select what they want, rather than trying to manage the practices. If they can do that faster, better, and cheaper than somebody else, great, but MSOs need to keep in mind that physicians have generally done a pretty good job of squeezing the excess out of their practices.
    —D. Louis Glaser, Esq., Partner
      Gardner, Carton & Douglas, Chicago, Illinois

In general, physicians who have chosen bits and pieces of our MSO appear to be more satisfied with the overall relationship, the money saved, and the scales of economy gained than physicians who take the entire spectrum of services. The reason behind this is that for physicians who select the full package of services, in essence, the MSO is taking on responsibility for all the overhead of the practice and it may be difficult to keep these physicians motivated to have a financial investment in the practice. It is also difficult to quantify the overall return and savings for practices that use the full array of MSO services, both for the MSO and the physicians. With the niche MSO products, you can easily quantify what you have saved the physician in terms of their time and costs.
    —Christopher Howard, Executive Vice President
      Health*first* Inc., Oklahoma City, Oklahoma

services, group purchasing for insurances, staff benefits purchasing, managed care contract evaluation, facility leasing, personnel management, and information systems. In essence, MSOs have evolved to provide niche products with demonstrated success, rather than promising to provide comprehensive practice management services to all physicians and failing to provide any or all of the services at acceptable levels.

The newer models of MSOs are developing increasingly refined cost-accounting and performance measurement systems

that will enable them to build the infrastructure needed to succeed at managed care contracting. Specific performance measures (e.g., collection rates and insurance costs) are demonstrated
in pre-financial and post-financial forecasts for the physician practice. Several years ago it was less critical to know where every
dollar and penny was spent, but with shrinking reimbursement,
increasing overhead costs, and inflation, MSOs have been forced
to move beyond elementary data analysis and become more accountable financially and demonstrate return on investment.

Argus Medical Management in Long Beach, California, is
an MSO that is owned equally by Catholic Healthcare West and
a 42-member physician group. A key facet of this MSO illustrates
why it can be characterized as a next-generation model: Argus
does not collect fees from its participating physicians unless it
can demonstrate that it has helped a practice improve its financial
performance by controlling shared group expenses and advising
physicians on strategies for limiting office overhead (Terry 1998).

William Beaumont Hospital in Royal Oak, Michigan, is developing an outreach program that, while not formally identified as an MSO, has the infrastructure to manage practices. This
program bucks the trend of offering cafeteria-style services in
favor of a package deal.

The program's structure reflects a lack of volume to offer niche
services and an effort to meet the needs of interested physicians.
A large hospital system in close proximity to William Beaumont
Hospital is facing the financial consequences of purchasing practices and employing physicians. As a hospital within this system
is closed and employed physicians are cut loose, formerly employed physicians need assistance in reestablishing private practices because they had relinquished this responsibility to the hospital system and do not want to assume the headaches of office
management. The William Beaumont Hospital offers practice
management services to select physicians, and in return physicians
pay the hospital for the costs of providing practice management

services at fair market value. The hospital's existing medical staff, all of whom are in private practice, are not interested in the practice management services because they have developed their management capabilities within their practices. The hospital acknowledges that it cannot perform these services any more efficiently than the established, private practice physicians.

MODEL #8: SELLING OR CONTRACTING OUTPATIENT
SERVICES TO PHYSICIANS

Some hospitals and health systems are seeking to maintain positive relationships with physicians by selling or contracting out select ambulatory services to the more entrepreneurial physicians. This approach is most frequently employed in situations where physicians express a strong interest in having a physician-controlled or physician-led service and hospitals elect to relinquish a service to physicians rather than engage in protracted battles that could permanently damage the relationships.

Some services inevitably migrate to an out-of-hospital setting. Hospitals and health systems that try to keep these and similar services in a hospital setting "at all costs" are often engaged in a losing battle. Even if the hospital wins the battle and retains the ambulatory service, it may lose opportunities to strengthen physician-hospital ties through other partnerships.

Hospitals and health systems that pursue selling or contracting outpatient services to physicians must carefully evaluate the pluses and minuses of these ventures and be wary of having too many of their services picked off in an attempt to appease physicians. However, hospitals may look at certain services and realize that while the service needs to be provided, the hospital is not excelling at managing and providing that level of care. In these specialized instances, such as with dialysis and radiology programs, it may make sense to sell or contract out that service to protect referrals and future business relationships with physicians.

SELLING OR CONTRACTING OUTPATIENT SERVICES TO PHYSICIANS:
VIEWS FROM THE INDUSTRY

Most hospital administrators that I have spoken with feel that twenty years down the road, there is going to be a significant portion of their outpatient services that will be joint ventured with companies, whether those are physician-owned companies or whether those are companies that then broker to physicians. But a partnership is a partnership. Few of those hospitals are planning to just totally sell out all of their services and become nothing more than an administrative broker for some small percentage. Instead, they are going to be looking for the true 50/50 ownership that a real partnership encompasses.

—Christopher Howard, Executive Vice President
Health*first* Inc., Oklahoma City, Oklahoma

There are instances where hospitals admit that they are struggling to offer a specialized service that could be provided better by someone else. But to say, gee, we're going to sell off one of our core services, such as ambulatory surgery, for no reason other than thinking that physicians aren't going to be loyal unless they get a piece of the action, that is a flawed strategy.

—D. Louis Glaser, Esq., Partner
Gardner, Carton & Douglas
Chicago, Illinois

Long Island College Hospital in Brooklyn, New York, elected to sell its outpatient dialysis services to a group of nephrologists for $18 million. The rationale for the sale was the realization that the true value the hospital placed on the service was the spin-off referrals. Ultimately the hospital decided that ensuring the loyalty of physicians and establishing a long-term linkage with them was more important than maintaining hospital control of outpatient dialysis services.

About 10 years ago, Genesee Hospital in Rochester, New York, contracted with a private radiology group to provide both technical and professional radiology services including CT scans, magnetic resonance imaging, ultrasound, and some general radiology capabilities. The hospital is now exploring similar arrangements for radiation oncology and dialysis services as well as outsourcing opportunities for other clinical services.

MODEL #9: CLINICAL LEADERSHIP COUNCILS

Physician participation in hospital or healthcare system administrative structures has traditionally been limited to medical director, vice president of medical affairs, or chief medical officer positions. Medical director positions are generally limited to a specific unit and focus primarily on defining policies and procedures. Physicians who serve as vice presidents of medical affairs assume dual roles in their positions. To maintain the respect of their peers, they must demonstrate clinical competency, but administrative demands may force them to abandon their practices. Meanwhile their peers tend to lump them into the category of hospital administrators rather than view them as medical staff representatives.

Clinical leadership councils are an emerging model for enhancing physician participation in governance and leadership roles. This model is in place at a few highly mature systems in the United States (Rutledge 1996). These councils usually include the chief executive of the physician organization, the hospital chief of staff, the chief medical officer or vice president for medical affairs, the primary care medical leader, and the vice president of patient care services. This group is generally charged with overseeing the cost and quality of all clinical operations for both inpatient and outpatient services (Rutledge 1996). Responsibilities that fall under this charge include fostering collaborative relationships among council members and the medical staff, assessing and monitoring outcomes within the system and in the community, and fulfilling a leadership role in the development and implementation of hospitalwide information systems.

These councils represent a giant leap of faith for hospitals and health systems because a number of decisions—particularly financial ones—that have historically remained under the purview of hospital administration are now put in the hands of physician and nursing leaders. Although this approach can be fraught with pitfalls and roadblocks, enormous potential exists for forging sustainable and powerful relationships with physician leaders and the medical staff who feel that they are finally appropriately represented at the top levels of the organization. Clinical leadership councils also help build trust on which to base other strategies of alignment and they are an excellent vehicle for quality improvement. Better care and service for patients can be achieved at a lower cost by improving patient care processes and quality and financial outcomes.

St. Joseph Mercy Hospital in Ann Arbor, Michigan, formed a clinical leadership council to help the system promote efficient movement of patients throughout the system and ensure a balance between quality and cost. The goal of the council was to reduce lengths of stay, costs per case, costs per day, and ancillary costs without sacrificing quality of care (Rutledge 1996).

To accomplish this goal, the hospital's CEO and chief financial officer have deferred many financial decisions to the council, which is ultimately responsible for total costs per case, resource allocation, and prioritizing capital expenditures. The council is given full access to management and financial data, including cost per case and per procedure by physician.

Not surprisingly, conflicting opinions and interests emerge when the council faces difficult decisions, such as what units should be closed or consolidated. But for physicians who have long bemoaned the fact that many administrative decisions are imposed on them, it is an opportunity to visibly shape healthcare delivery.

MODEL #10: PHYSICIAN RELATIONS AND
RESPONSIVENESS PROGRAMS

Before the days of more formalized alliances between hospitals
and physicians, physician relations programs functioned as
one of the few formal linkages between physicians and hospitals. Many hospitals viewed these programs as a tool for staying
in touch with physicians through newsletters, letters, phone
calls, and visits to physicians from hospital "sales" representatives.

These programs have been historically difficult to implement
because they require high levels of personal attention and effort
to ascertain the needs and interests of physicians, particularly
the key admitters to the hospital. Hospitals and health systems
have also realized that if you dominate enough of the market
and have system scale, you can create a market presence that
compels physicians to align with you.

Many physicians are now expressing interest in hospital responsiveness to practice-specific concerns and needs. In an attempt to address requests for improved hospital responsiveness,
some hospitals and health systems are reexamining their physician relations programs to see if the programs can be retooled to
serve as valuable forums for interfacing with physicians and earning and building loyalty, trust, and commitment.

These new programs encompass a number of activities:

• Personal meetings between physicians and senior-level
  hospital administrators that are brief, "to the point," and
  focus on true dialogue about improvements the hospital
  should pursue to better support practices. Examples of
  practice support initiatives, which can emanate from
  these dialogs, include protected block time for high-uti-
  lization surgeons, emergency room fast-track services,
  and daily call-back programs;

PHYSICIAN RELATIONS AND RESPONSIVENESS PROGRAMS:
VIEWS FROM THE INDUSTRY

If you want to have good relations with the typical physician who is
very busy in his or her practice and has very little free time these
days, the key is to not waste their time.
  —Adam Henick, Executive Director
    Montefiore Medical Group, New York, New York

Hospitals and health care systems are finding it harder and harder
to fund physician relationship programs because it is pure overhead. What I'm not finding is a more sophisticated physician or
provider relations approach than I did 10 years ago. You would think
in 10 years that part of the industry would have become more sophisticated in this area because in many cases, it's the only way to
differentiate yourself from the competition.
  —Christopher Howard, Executive Vice President
    Health*first* Inc., Oklahoma City, Oklahoma

- Task force spin-offs to provide a forum for physician input
  into strategic planning and other key hospital initiatives;
- Staff complaint protocols, response guidelines (e.g., a
  phone call within 24 hours), and physician surveys to
  provide multiple avenues for feedback; and
- Monitoring of the effects of program offerings such as
  improvement in operations and systems performance,
  levels of patient satisfaction, emergency room waiting
  times, and operating room utilization.

The more successful physician relations programs reflect the
philosophy that everyone is responsible for physician relations
(i.e., "it's an attitude, not a program") and that earning physician
loyalty is a long-term process that can be destroyed in a nanosec-
ond if demonstrated responsiveness is lacking. Although these

programs do add overhead costs and may be subject to return-on-investment (ROI) evaluation, when compared to the dollars lost on failed acquisition strategies, the value added by these programs may be worth the investment. It is important to note that once these programs are initiated and formalized, expectations are raised about correcting identified inefficiencies. Programs should not be started until hospitals or systems are ready to make a firm commitment to address physicians' concerns.

A four-hospital system in New England demonstrates the ineffectiveness of some physician relations programs. The program was failing because its four hospital representatives were perceived to be spies that generally focused on topics of interest to the hospital (principally how to generate referrals), not necessarily on issues of importance to physicians. Most of the assignments the representatives received were at the crisis stage, instead of allowing them to intervene at a point where the relationship had a better chance of survival.

A teaching hospital in the Southwest has a vastly different physician relations program in place. It is a decentralized program with eight staff members that focus primarily (80 percent) on primary care physicians. The representatives employ the 80:20 listen-to-talk rule and the number of visits and outcomes are centrally monitored and data are used effectively to support resolution of issues. When the hospital was seeking ways to trim overhead, the program was nearly terminated until the value of its services survived an ROI evaluation.

NEXT-GENERATION MODELS IN ACTION

The models presented represent a wide array of partnership options with varying levels of financial investment, different degrees of integration achieved, and uncertainty about the staying power or long-term consequences of the models. Some models may only be appropriate in highly unique situations where both

the hospital or health system and physicians have carefully performed an honest assessment of the options. And some models
merely represent ground-level starting points for building more
creative and perhaps tightly coupled relationships in the future.

As hospitals, health systems, and physicians examine these
potential partnership models and begin to brainstorm about other
potential physician–health system relationships, the following
questions must be thoughtfully and honestly addressed:

- Will the financial investment required by the partnership be recoverable?
- Can the partnership model evolve as the market and
  goals and objectives change over time? Will the partnership model periodically be reexamined to ascertain
  whether it continues to fulfill expectations?
- Is the partnership sustainable over the long-term? If not,
  will short-term gains offset the brief nature of the partnership?
- Does the partnership conform to the overall strategic
  direction set for the hospital or system?
- Does the partnership place all participants in an equal
  position of risk and reward?
- If the partnership is forged with a select group of physicians, how will the hospital's or system's relationships
  with their remaining physicians be affected?
- If the partnership fails, can it be dissolved and what will
  be the consequences?

When open, honest, and productive discussions occur about
the full range of benefits and consequences of physician–health
system partnerships, providers are taking the valuable first step
in working together to nurture and sustain their presence in the
healthcare delivery system of the future, regardless of the partnership model that is selected.

REFERENCES

Alexander, J., T. Vaughn, L. Burns, H. Zuckerman, R. Andersen, P. Torrens, and D. Hilberman. 1996. "Organizational Approaches to Integrated Health Care Delivery: A Taxonomic Analysis of Physician-Organization Arrangements." *Medical Care Research and Review* 53 (1): 71–93.

Center for Health Policy Research. 1998. *Socioeconomic Characteristics of Medical Practice 1997/98*, 21. Chicago: American Medical Association.

Cockley, D., M. Riddell, A. Kaluzny, and H. Zuckerman. 1995. *Barriers and Facilitators to Physician Participation in Integrated Delivery Systems*. Chapel Hill, NC; Cecil G. Sheps Center for Health Services Research, University of North Carolina at Chapel Hill.

Dynan, L., G. Bazzoli, L. Burns. 1998. "Assessing the Extent of Integration Achieved through Physician-Hospital Arrangements." *Journal of Healthcare Management* 43 (3): 257.

Health Care Advisory Board Executive Briefing. 1999. *The Physician Perspective Key Drivers of Physician Loyalty*, 42. Washington, D.C.: The Advisory Board.

Institute for the Future. 1998. *A Forecast of Health Care in America*, 48. New Brunswick, NJ: Robert Wood Johnson Foundation.

Rutledge, V.R. 1996. "Hospital/Physician Alignment: A Model for Success." *Oncology Issues* 11 (6): 18–20.

Terry, K. 1999. "Capitation on the Rise." *Medical Economics* 76 (23): 188.

Terry, K. 1998. "Now Hospitals Want to be Your Partner, Not Your Boss." *Medical Economics* 75 (16): 81.

Zuckerman, H., D. Hilberman, R. Andersen, L. Burns, J. Alexander, and P. Torrens. 1998. "Physicians and Organizations: Strange Bedfellows or a Marriage Made in Heaven?" *Frontiers of Health Services Management* 14 (3): 3–34.

4

Legal Considerations for Next-Generation Physician–Health System Partnerships

CONTRIBUTED BY

Scott D. Godshall, Esq., Attorney-at-Law,
Pepper Hamilton LLP, Philadelphia

HOSPITALS AND PHYSICIANS exploring partnership relationships face an impressive array of Byzantine regulatory structures that must be addressed before the partnerships become done deals. The primary regulations—the Anti-Kickback Statute, Stark II regulations, Internal Revenue Service (IRS) inurement regulations, and the Civil Monetary Penalties Statutes—are hurdles that should be surmounted by legal counsel each time a new affiliation relationship is on the table.

These regulations on an individual basis are highly complex, and as a group they present conflicting and inconsistent rules and standards for physician–health system affiliations. The delay and expense regulations impose on partnerships might be easier to accept if the outcome was a reasonable level of certainty that an affiliation meets regulatory muster. Instead, certainty recedes as enforcement activity grows. Such uncertainty has not, by any means, restricted innovation. Many variations of joint ventures and reengineering of acquired physician practices are being practiced nationwide.

To help healthcare professionals and physicians understand how to structure partnerships that will pass regulatory scrutiny, this chapter will discuss the four main regulatory schemes, present some general guidelines for physician–health system affiliations, and provide an overview of joint operating agreements—an affiliation model that is likely to increase in popularity in the coming years.

Anti-Kickback Statute

The Anti-Kickback Statute generally prohibits the knowing and willful receipt or payment of remuneration for, or to induce the referral of an individual for the furnishing of, or the purchasing, leasing, ordering, or arranging for or recommending of, any good or service for which payment may be made under the Medicare and Medicaid programs. The statute, in short, prohibits a hospital from purchasing referrals and stops a physician from selling them. For example, "consulting" positions for physicians where the physicians provide no services are not acceptable when the purpose of the agreements is to compensate physicians for making referrals to the hospitals for which the physicians are consulting.

The Anti-Kickback Statute includes five exceptions for certain discounts, group purchasing organizations, employment relationships, waivers of certain coinsurance payments, and for specific practices set forth by the U.S. Department of Health and Human Services (DHHS) in the Safe Harbor Regulations. The Health Insurance Portability and Accountability Act of 1996 (the

Health Care Reform Act) added a sixth exception for written agreements involving risk-sharing arrangements.

A limited number of judicial decisions have interpreted the scope of the Anti-Kickback Statute and emphasize that a court evaluating a provider's liability under the Anti-Kickback Statute should focus on the provider's intent in entering into the relationship with physicians. Courts applying the Anti-Kickback Statute have generally applied it broadly, holding that the law can be violated if "one purpose" of a payment is to induce referrals from the recipient of the payment to the person or entity that makes the payment. Other courts have focused on the "knowing and willful" element of the statute and have required that for a violation to occur, a person must know that the statute prohibits remuneration to induce referrals and engage in prohibited conduct "with the specific intent to disobey the law." The applicable standard, in other words, varies from court to court and state to state. But the bottom line rarely varies: an intent to buy patient referrals poisons virtually any proposed physician–health system venture.

Physician employment, management, or services agreements may be structured to comply with the Anti-Kickback Statute, provided that the agreements fall within the safe harbors promulgated by the DHHS. The personal services and management contracts' safe harbor, for example, would apply to a medical director's agreement between a hospital or hospital subsidiary and an independent physician. This safe harbor shields providers from the anti-kickback liability if the agreement meets the following conditions:

- A written agreement that specifies the services to be provided is signed by the parties.
- If the services are part-time, the agreement specifies the schedule.

- The agreement lasts at least one year.
- The agreement does not involve services to promote illegal activity.
- Most importantly, compensation is set in advance, consistent with fair market value in an "arms-length" transaction (negotiated in good faith), and not determined in a manner that takes into account the volume or value of referrals.

Self-Referral Statute (Stark II Regulations)

The Self-Referral Statute, sometimes referred to as the Stark Law, prohibits physicians from making referrals to entities for the furnishing of "designated health services" for which payments may be made under the Medicare or Medicaid programs, if the physicians or immediate family members of the physicians have "financial relationships" with the entities, unless one of several exceptions are met. The term "designated health services" includes inpatient and outpatient hospital services, and the term "financial relationship" includes an ownership interest in or a compensation arrangement with (including the payment of any form of remuneration by) the entity.

Because a physician employment, management, or service agreement creates a financial relationship within the definition of the Self-Referral Statute, the statute would prohibit a physician from referring patients to a hospital that participates in such an agreement for designated health services. These services are defined by the Self-Referral Statute to include inpatient health services, physical therapy, home health services, and clinical laboratory services, among others, unless the relationships created by the agreements fit within one of the exceptions built into the statute.

Like the Anti-Kickback Statute, the Self-Referral Statute provides for exceptions, meaning that the statute will permit otherwise prohibited referrals if certain conditions are met. Where an individual physician provides medical or management services to a physician–health system joint venture, the most likely exception will be the personal services exception. To qualify, a physician–health system agreement must satisfy at least the following requirements:

- The agreement must be in writing and signed by the parties.
- The agreement must specify the services covered and must cover all of the services to be provided by the physician (or an immediate family member).
- Aggregate services contracted for may not exceed those that are reasonable and necessary for the legitimate business purposes of the arrangement.
- The term of the arrangement must be for at least one year.
- Compensation paid over the term of the arrangement must be set in advance, may not exceed fair market value, and (except for physician incentive plan payments) may not be determined in a manner that takes into account the volume or value of referrals or other business generated between the parties.
- The agreement must specify that the services may not involve an arrangement that violates any federal or state law and must meet any other requirements that may be imposed by local, state, and federal regulation.

IRS Self-Inurement Regulations

Additional requirements for physician–health system affiliations may arise for any provider exempt from federal income tax as a charitable organization described in section 501(c)(3) of the Internal Revenue Code. In promoting their charitable purposes, exempt organizations may not permit their income or assets to be used to benefit private individuals or entities, including physicians employed by exempt organizations and physician practices acquired by exempt organizations.

Almost any benefit to a physician may jeopardize an organization's exemption. For example, inurement or private benefit could occur if, as part of entering into a relationship with a physician, a hospital provider was to provide goods or services to a physician for less than fair market value or to pay more than fair market value for goods or services it receives from a physician. Fair market value typically is defined by the IRS as the price on which a willing buyer and a willing seller would agree, neither being under any compulsion to buy or sell, and both having reasonable knowledge of the relevant facts.

Civil Monetary Penalties Statute Law

The Civil Monetary Penalties Law (CMP) provisions of the Social Security Act prohibit any hospital from knowingly making a payment directly or indirectly to physicians as inducements to reduce or limit services Medicare or Medicaid patients receive under physicians' care. Any incentive plan that rewards physicians for reducing or limiting care violates this statute.

Perhaps the most well-known application of the CMP provisions to a physician–health system venture occurred with respect to gainsharing. On July 8, 1999, the DHHS Inspector General's Office issued a special advisory bulletin announcing its opinion that the CMP provisions bar gainsharing arrangements. These arrangements, in most healthcare variations, include an agreement by physicians to assist in reducing hospital costs in exchange for sharing in the financial benefits of that cost reduction. Because gainsharing compensates physicians for reducing the costs of items and services to Medicare and Medicaid patients, the Inspector General concluded — notwithstanding widespread use of gainsharing throughout the country—that gainsharing violates the CMP provisions.

GENERAL GUIDELINES FOR PHYSICIAN—HEALTH SYSTEM AFFILIATIONS

While the regulations covering physician–health system affiliations are highly complex, they are not inscrutable. As hospitals, health systems, and physicians explore the various models for affiliation, they should start with these straightforward guidelines:

- Do not try to buy patients, either overtly or covertly. No aspect of physician compensation, direct or indirect, under a physician–health system venture, may be tied to the volume or value of physician referrals. Do not use physician arrangements to buy patient referrals.
- Develop a business plan first. The absence of a valid business plan for a physician arrangement will uniformly give rise to the inference that the primary purpose of the arrangement is to buy patient referrals. Any arrangement begun with this goal in mind is impermissible. Other goals—improving quality, tightening adherence to clinical protocols, or achieving operational ends (reducing costs)—that are reasonably developed and reasonably applied will not give rise to this inference and should survive scrutiny.
- Document the business plan. Few meaningful business plans go far without being committed to writing. Few successful plans fail to go through rigorous analysis, whether that analysis takes the form of preparing pro forma financial statements, securing independent valuation or legal opinions, or documenting some other written follow-up. Business plans that are not documented in this fashion may suggest that the plan itself was not

taken seriously; arrangements created and dollars exchanged under such a plan may invite heightened regulatory scrutiny.

- Consult counsel early. Asking legal counsel to "find a way" to approve hand-shake deals is ineffective and dangerous. Bring counsel in during development of the business plan, before it is applied.
- Keep it at arms-length. What is a fair price for the physician services for which the hospital is contracting? Hospitals, health systems, and physicians need to perform an analysis of compensation levels that can be put in writing and supported by third-party documentation.
- Do not buy cost-savings. The CMP's broad provisions arose from intense public dissatisfaction with perceptions that both payors and providers were improperly restricting or denying necessary and appropriate medical care to cut costs. Do not enter into physician ventures that may be interpreted as motivating physicians to take steps that may result in reduced care.

These guidelines are not intended to take the place of detailed legal analysis; they are instead intended to provide the nonlawyer with a general framework that facilitates understanding of some of the key factors likely to drive the legal analysis of physician–health system arrangements.

JOINT OPERATING AGREEMENTS

Joint operating agreements (JOAs) are legally binding contracts or documented agreements that detail the terms and conditions and rights and responsibilities to jointly develop, provide, or manage a service.

Many physician–health system JOAs involve admitting physicians managing certain aspects of hospitals' clinical operations.

The managed aspects may range from simple operating room coordination to the development of clinical care guidelines.

From the perspective of improving physician–health system relationships, successful joint operating agreements focus on making hospitals more attractive places for physicians to treat patients because of higher levels of physician involvement in and management of patient care. From a legal perspective, such agreements generally make a far more presentable case by clearing many of the regulatory hurdles for physician–health system affiliations.

By applying the guidelines discussed in this chapter, a comparison can be conducted of a joint operating agreement that is successful from the perspectives of the hospital, physicians, and legal counsel versus one that is not.

Gainsharing is one type of joint operating agreement that refers to any number of models developed to join physicians and hospitals together to achieve cost savings for hospitals. The benefits of the cost savings (dollars saved) are divided between the participating physicians and the hospital. Gainsharing arrangements, whether in the form of a cost-management contract, a risk pool, or a legally distinct joint venture, all share the same fundamental premise: motivate physicians to reduce costs by giving them a healthy share of the cost savings.

Based on guidelines previously discussed, it is apparent that gainsharing can meet all but one of the requirements. With appropriate caps and other adjustments, the arrangement need not be tied to the volume or value of referrals from participating physicians. Good gainsharing plans usually develop from an easily understood and easily documented business plan: cut costs and save money. And the financial terms can be tied to third-party valuations such as the purchase price of equipment and reimbursement rates from Medicare. Given these characteristics, it is not surprising that gainsharing in the mid-1990s was so widely implemented.

The problem with gainsharing, from a legal perspective, is that it may result in the reduction of services to patients, including Medicare or Medicaid patients. Gainsharing explicitly triggers cost reductions and, generally speaking, runs the risk of achieving these cost savings by reducing services. Motivating physicians to reduce services violates the CMP; on this ground the DHHS Inspector General's Office has barred gainsharing arrangements.

A better joint operating arrangement shifts the focus from hospital costs—something usually not on the physician's radar screen nor within their experience to judge and evaluate—to hospital effectiveness, something that is on every staff physician's radar screen. One urban hospital group in the Northeast concluded that the most significant threat to its outpatient surgery operations was the fact that its administrative and operational procedures were not physician friendly. An important specialty group was considering taking its surgery elsewhere, citing the lack of dedicated operating room time, the wide variation in surgery time among other specialists performing the same procedures, the commingling of outpatients with acute care inpatients, and the general condition and atmosphere of the outpatient facilities.

The hospitals responded by proposing a joint operating agreement to manage the outpatient surgery facility with the physicians. The hospitals organized a physician clinical guidelines committee to create new clinical guidelines, work with the hospital to redesign the physical facilities, and take a variety of steps to make the outpatient facilities more patient friendly. The result of greater physician involvement has been increased use of the facilities and more outpatient revenue for the hospitals. The specialists found their patients requesting that procedures be performed at these hospitals to enjoy the better treatment.

From a legal perspective, such a joint operating agreement has all the qualities of gainsharing without risking a reduction of care. The sensible, easy-to-understand business strategy (increase volume by improving patient satisfaction) involves no purchase of referrals. To the extent that physicians require reimbursement for the time they devote to management, a reliable third-party appraisal of the value of physicians' time (not of their patient referrals) was used.

CONCLUSION

The legal framework for physician–health system relationships, as complex as it is, will ultimately support the strengthening of these affiliations and ensure that standards of patient care are not compromised. The key is the strategy used to improve these relationships. Legal analysis often will support rather than inhibit a well-developed strategy (for example, one that focuses on patient satisfaction rather than physician referrals). With the help of experienced legal counsel, hospitals and physicians will have access to the statutory and regulatory tools necessary to make viable strategies work and foster the implementation of next-generation physician–health system partnership models.

Case Study: Successful Financial Performance Improvement and Next-Generation Partnership Models for a Primary Care Network

CONTRIBUTED BY

Christopher Howard, Executive Vice President,
Health*first* Inc., Oklahoma City

DURING THE 1990S, hospitals and health systems across the country rushed to form networks of primary care physicians and subspecialists. Driven by fears of eroding referral bases, lagging managed care clout, and threats from aggressive competitors, primary care networks have established employment or management relationships with physicians—relationships that have failed on a number of fronts, but most markedly have been financially disastrous.

This chapter illustrates how a primary care network took bold steps in recognizing its shortcomings and rebuilding itself to be a competitive, financially sound venture for both its employed and managed physicians and its sponsoring health system.

97

HISTORIC PERSPECTIVE

Health*first* Physician Management Services, Inc., was formed in 1993 under the name of Healthcare Systems of Oklahoma, Inc., a for-profit corporation that resided under the corporate umbrella of SSM Health Care of Oklahoma, a not-for-profit corporation. SSM Health Care of Oklahoma operates as a subsidiary corporation to the SSM Health Care System, a multistate healthcare system based in St. Louis, Missouri. Although the Healthcare Systems of Oklahoma corporation had existed since 1985, it was restructured in 1993 to serve as the physician organization for SSM Health Care of Oklahoma.

The initial purpose of Healthcare Systems of Oklahoma was to provide network formation assistance, practice management support, physician recruitment and development, and managed care administration for St. Anthony Hospital, a 644-bed not-for-profit tertiary care facility located in downtown Oklahoma City.

As was the case with many large hospitals in the early 1990s, St. Anthony aspired to solidify its market position by developing a primary care network that would protect its market and managed care position. Although the hospital had taken initial steps into the business of employing, managing, or otherwise contracting with primary care physicians, it was not until 1993 that senior administration decided to aggressively pursue development of a physician network that could support St. Anthony Hospital and any hospital partners it might affiliate with in the future.

From 1993 to 1996, St. Anthony saw dramatic growth not only in its own business but through business acquired via mergers with Bone and Joint Hospital and Hillcrest Health Center and an affiliation with Mission Hill Memorial Hospital in Shawnee, Oklahoma. As the hospital system grew, so did the number of physicians in the managed care network. Healthcare Systems of Oklahoma, having been restructured as a physician-hospital organization and management services organization, began aggressively developing a large physician network by recruiting a physician panel to use to contract with HMOs in the Oklahoma City market. The initial managed care network had 250 physicians, including 60 primary care physicians.

During this time, senior administration began to formulate a strategy to secure the loyalty and viability of the managed care network by bolstering it with physicians employed or managed by Healthcare Systems of Oklahoma. From 1993 to 1996, the network grew from 10 employed or managed physicians to a network that encompassed over 100 employed or managed physicians, with over 70 primary care physicians.

Today, Healthcare Systems of Oklahoma manages the network via a subsidiary management services organization (MSO), and also has ownership in several buildings, a pharmacy, and various other revenue-generating ventures that contribute to the financial stability of Healthcare Systems of Oklahoma. These investments include partial ownership in a durable medical equipment company, a surgery center, a managed care administrative service, and a central physician office billing service, which on a combined basis generates over $1 million dollars in net operating profit for Healthcare Systems of Oklahoma's MSO. Annual revenue for the MSO in 1999 exceeded $23 million dollars. The growth of the MSO has been nothing short of meteoric; however, it has been accompanied by the standard set of operational, structural, and financial issues that are typical of a rapidly developing MSO and primary care network.

FLAWS IN INITIAL STRUCTURE

From 1993 to 1997 the Healthcare Systems of Oklahoma physician network and related management services organization experienced tremendous growth. This growth was planned as SSM Health Care of Oklahoma, with St. Anthony as its anchor company, was facing dire circumstances as an inner-city hospital with eroding market share. Aggressive competitors had surrounded the city with suburban-based healthcare facilities and services, choking St. Anthony's patient and physician supply.

To combat this situation, St. Anthony had to be proactive in creating a dedicated physician base that could partner with the hospital to combat the competitive forces that were weakening the system. SSM Health Care of Oklahoma created a strategic physician development plan that called for funding of up to $20 million dollars to create and support a physician network dedicated to the system, including $17 million for practice development and $3 million for development of a management services organization infrastructure. The plan was implemented in 1993 and resulted in a network of employed and managed primary care physicians that grew at a rate of approximately 20 physicians per year over the next three years.

To cope with this dramatic growth, Healthcare Systems of Oklahoma was quickly organized into a managed care and physician practice support vehicle for the system. The rapid growth was unavoidable because of market conditions, and Healthcare Systems of Oklahoma incurred many of the same growing pains experienced by similar companies established by hospital-based systems.

Characteristics such as inexperienced practice management and billing staff, too few management support staff, significant losses associated with owned or managed practices because of low productivity and volume, and physician dissension were common to Healthcare Systems of Oklahoma in its early years. Initially Healthcare Systems of Oklahoma was plagued with:

- Inexperienced staff;
- Rapid growth and poor location;
- Unaligned economic incentives;
- Lack of both physician participation and leadership to address critical issues; and
- Lack of preparedness for divestiture.

Inexperienced Staff

As was the case with many hospital-sponsored physician organizations in the early 1990s, St. Anthony/SSM Health Care of Oklahoma began developing its physician support services division and employed physician network through the efforts of hospital-based employees who formed the initial infrastructure of Healthcare Systems of Oklahoma. This approach accommodated the initial needs of the system with respect to senior administration; however, hiring hospital-based employees into physician practices and physician practice support services limited the initial performance and effectiveness of the organization. Support employees struggled to understand issues related to physician practices that were much different than those they had experienced while employed in the hospital setting. This "culture shock" was most evident among former hospital business office personnel who were experienced in billing and accounts receivable management for claims that typically exceeded $500. These employees struggled to adapt to the physician practice environment where accounts of $60 or less constituted the majority of the day-to-day billing and collections process and supply orders were often $200 instead of thousands of dollars. Overall, former hospital employees struggled to adapt to the low-cost, lower-volume world of physician practice management.

Rapid Growth and Poor Location

The rate of growth within the physician network was significantly more dramatic than originally anticipated by administrative officials at St. Anthony Hospital or Healthcare Systems of Oklahoma. The network grew from a handful of primary care physicians to over 50 employed or managed physicians within two years because of a high level of physician interest. The anticipated and budgeted growth rate for the first few years of operation was expected to be the recruitment and addition of 10 employed or managed physicians per year.

This unexpected growth taxed the ability of Healthcare Systems of Oklahoma to effectively provide administrative management support to the physicians who had joined the network via recruitment efforts. The network not only faced the growing problem of having a rapidly expanding practice support company with support employees who were better suited to hospital environments, but now struggled with not having enough employees to handle the influx of physicians.

A central billing company was formed to support the network, but its performance lagged because of inexperienced personnel, many of whom were former hospital employees, and an inability to maintain trained staff from month to month. It was a common misperception in the early days of the physician network that recruiting, hiring, and placing skilled practice management staff would not be difficult. In fact, the Oklahoma City market (like many others) did not have an abundance of available employees with expertise in physician-office management. The network resorted to hiring untrained employees and putting them through a crash course of practice employment training. Locating skilled employees continues to be a major initiative for the network.

The massive effort to build employment or management agreements with primary care physicians led to several physicians being brought into the network primarily because of their interest and willingness to work as a partner with St. Anthony, rather than for the strategic location of the practices. The hospital had seen significant patient base erosion in the 10 years leading up to the development of Healthcare Systems of Oklahoma, largely as a result of outmigration of physicians and citizens from the downtown area, and was eager to recruit many physicians to help replenish its eroded market share. The result was a frantic pace of physician-relationship building that led to the acquisition or recruitment of several practices that had little potential for being successful operationally or financially because of poor location. Significant allocation of human resources to help in marketing, relationship building, and image building to help create business in these strategically disadvantaged practices produced negative or neutral returns on investment and pulled valuable human resources from other practices.

Unaligned Economic Incentives

The early rush to develop a primary care network and the weakened financial position of the system's anchor hospital led to several contractual relationships with physicians that would prove to be economically nonviable. Contracts that were based on historic economic data (i.e., "peak performance") would at times prove to be unrealistic as market conditions, new contracts, or practice changes led to performance that did not meet expectations. The resulting management activity to correct poorly performing practices would prove to be the single largest allocation of practice management time and expense. Worse yet, contracts that failed to align the economic incentives between the hospital and physicians led to the development of a group physician culture that was disjointed with that of hospital and physician management representatives.

Lack of Physician Participation and Leadership to Address Critical Issues

In 1993, a board of directors was named for Healthcare Systems of Oklahoma. The original structure called for a major hospital management presence, and significant physician (both specialist and primary care) participation. In 1993, St. Anthony did not have strong primary care physician leadership, thus initially the board had hospital, specialist, and primary care representatives, but was better suited to focus on hospital or specialist issues than primary care issues.

The shortage of primary care physicians in the initial days of the Healthcare Systems of Oklahoma managed care network did not just affect the operations of the board. Indeed, it also led to slow growth in managed care plans that required an abundance of primary care gatekeepers. Practice management officials were forced to make major policy decisions with little input from the primary care physician base of Healthcare Systems of Oklahoma. The organization also exhibited traits one would expect from an entity dominated by specialists and hospital administrators. Issues related to patient care delivery for the hospital and specialists took precedence over many of the major concerns of primary care physicians.

In the managed care network, this tendency was most evident in the high utilization experienced in the physician offices and in the hospital network. In other areas, such as the major policy decision making of the organization, matters of volume and growth of business were prioritized over building an organization that would meet the demands for preventive health maintenance, accountability for community health, and other traits common to advanced healthcare environments.

Lack of Preparedness for Divestiture

Creating strong physician and administrative leadership was only one challenge faced by Healthcare Systems of Oklahoma in its early days. A tremendous amount of time and energy was spent building a core group of physicians in practice and leadership positions who would be dedicated to reestablishing the system as an Oklahoma City health provider. But the system was not prepared to address the inevitable unwinding or divestiture of relationships that, for a variety of reasons, could not continue.

Most of the physicians recruited to be a part of the Healthcare Systems of Oklahoma network have performed well and were still with the network in 1999; however, in a few instances the best interests of both parties were better served by dissolving the relationship to sustain the overall well-being of the physician organization's culture. Healthcare Systems of Oklahoma was initially unprepared to handle such issues as the loss of business to hospital affiliates, loss of physicians to the managed care network, erosion of critical physician leadership, and criticism of the management team.

With time, network management learned valuable lessons about the unfortunate but sometimes necessary divestiture of physician relationships. The most critical, often overlooked lesson was to adequately prepare the physician, his or her staff, and the hospital administration for the changes that will occur or might occur if improvement could not be demonstrated. Healthcare Systems of Oklahoma learned that physicians who are knowledgeable of their current situations are much more agreeable when difficult items relative to their practices must be discussed. Hospital administrators, however, are much more agreeable to the possible loss of staff physicians when the potential and tangible effects of their departures can be quantified.

With time, preparation, and attention to the divestiture process, the network has revealed that the effect on the hospital partners was fairly minimal compared to the amount of concern shown for the potential loss of business relationships. In fact, most of the physicians who were divested of the network have stayed aligned with the hospital partners, choosing instead to look for other creative ways to maintain relationships with the system, even if under very different circumstances than in the past.

RESTRUCTURING THE NETWORK

In early 1995, a comprehensive analysis of Healthcare Systems of Oklahoma, including the physician network, the managed care network, and the physician practice management support infrastructure, was performed to determine what corrective changes could be made to enhance the system as a whole. The analysis was performed by an external firm that organized data and input from administrative and physician officials.

Following this review, a corrective action plan was created by senior administration that called for a completely restructured physician organization. This organization would have significant primary care leadership, a professional administration team with group physician practice management backgrounds, and a managed care support division staffed with managed care and other high-risk insurance experts.

The plan, created in early 1995, was bold in that it initially called for the creation of an equity model management services organization that would provide employed or managed physicians with financial incentives to help correct losses in their practices. As this plan was being created, the practice management losses for the system had grown to over $4.5 million dollars per year. Significant and immediate corrective action would have to be taken if the physician network was to remain financially viable; however, each individual employed or managed physician would, through the proposed structure, have the opportunity to share financially if their practice should become profitable in the future. Figure 5-1 illustrates the financial performance of the network.

THE RESTRUCTURING PLAN

Focus groups comprised of physicians and administration began organizing what would ultimately become a template for a new physician services organization. The new organization was

FIGURE 5.1   Health*first* Network Performance Total Expenditures

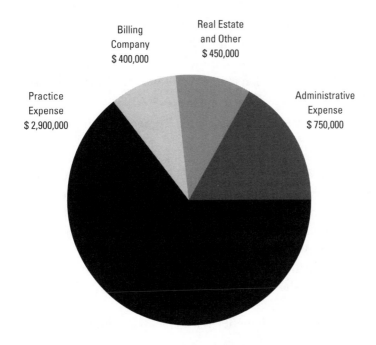

given a name, Health*first* Physician Management Services, Inc. Health*first* was described as a management services organization for the ssm Health Care of Oklahoma healthcare system. Its initial purposes were to provide practice management services to those physicians whose practices were owned or managed by the system, provide managed care formation and management services to the physician-hospital managed care network, and direct physician recruitment and development for the system.

To achieve these objectives and stay focused on physician needs, a new set of committees was designed to govern turnaround and ongoing management activity. The new committees included operations improvement, contracting, utilization review/quality assurance, and patient care. These initial committees were instrumental in developing the template for what would soon become a physician-led, professionally managed organization capable of not only providing high-quality healthcare services to the community, but also extending efficient and effective practice management and managed care support services to members of the physician network.

The initial restructuring plan outlined several key targets that would receive concentrated improvement efforts. These targets were selected to address the organization's key deficiencies in its early phase, such as poor financial performance by the owned and managed physician practices, a weak managed care network dominated by specialists at the expense of primary care physicians, and a pervasive feeling on behalf of physicians and hospital administration alike that the organization was simply not meeting the needs of the system. The organization realignment objectives addressed the following issues:

- Organization of physician leadership and building trust;
- Development of an effective committee structure;
- Improvement of operations support functions and staff;
- Alignment of economic incentives between physicians and the system;
- Operational expectations;
- Provision of timely and accurate data to physicians;
- A focus on process and goals; and
- Divestiture plans, when necessary.

Organization of Physician Leadership and Building Trust

In the early days of the restructuring effort, initiatives focused on identifying a core group of physician leaders who would commit their time and energy to developing a better model for operational and financial success. This was not an easy task since the physician organization was initially dominated by specialists and hospital representatives. But the organization knew it had to identify and empower primary care leaders who had the unique ability to focus on finding solutions that would mutually benefit all participating physicians.

This arduous identification process took almost six months. An initial core group of four primary care physician leaders who could objectively look at plans met with three hospital system representatives and three specialists. The group was thus able to propose structural solutions from three perspectives.

This mix of administrators and physicians may at first glance appear to be imbalanced, but the members proved to be supportive of each other's perspectives. In retrospect, the selection of the physician leaders was the single most-important task of the early restructuring process. Thoughtful selection of these leaders resulted in a core group of individuals with the unique ability to consider the needs of the system, primary care physicians, and specialists without allowing their individual concerns and needs to dominate the restructuring process. These physicians created policies that reflected a culture of equality and selflessness; these values remain as founding principles of the organization.

Though unwritten, the selection criterion for board and committee members of Health*first* continues to emphasize that individuals have the ability to discuss, make decisions, and form policy for the organization in a manner that will balance the benefits for all three partners. This approach has ensured that the organizational culture is one of mutual respect and trust among partners, a characteristic that was absent in the organization before 1995.

Development of an Effective Committee Structure

The initial restructuring efforts of the company focused on two distinct areas. The first effort focused on the reorganization of the managed care division. This division provides administrative support services to the physician management organization that today encompasses over 500 physicians (including 140 primary care physicians) and manages 25,000 capitated lives.

The second phase of operational restructuring involved the practice management support division, and included the creation of a central billing company to support all physicians employed or managed by the system.

The first steps undertaken to begin improving the practice management/managed care administrative divisions as a whole were the selection and formation of a primary care group that could help lead the restructuring necessary to help accomplish the organization's goals. A group of employed and managed physicians formed First Physicians Medical Group and provided the nucleus of primary care leadership that oversaw the remaining improvement activities. First Physicians Medical Group elected a small executive committee to lead the board and committee restructuring of Health*first*. Each restructured committee was designed and staffed by an administrative and medical leadership team that was dominated by primary care physicians but included subspecialists and hospital officials eager to improve the overall activities of the system.

All the committees aggressively pursued their initiatives, but the operations improvement committee had the greatest effect on the organization's budget. This committee's single purpose was to reduce the operating losses of practices employed or managed by the SSM Health Care of Oklahoma system. The committee targeted practices for financial improvement and worked with senior practice management personnel to create a series of practice management reports that would help the committee focus its efforts on reducing operational losses.

The primary purpose of these reports is to provide accurate and concise data to both management staff and physicians. This information is in turn used to determine the current economic health of each practice as well as the practice's trends over the previous year. The key goal for the reports was simplicity. The primary report, the Practice Performance Report, needed to provide quick and easy references on practice performance. This report format, now used by Health*first* and presented in Figure 5-2, focuses on the most basic practice health indicators and matches data to nationally accepted statistical norms provided by the Medical Group Management Association. The report enables physicians to quickly ascertain how their practice is performing and at what percentile of the normal performance indicators for a physician practicing medicine in their specialty within the Oklahoma City region.

Using data from the new reports, each practice was reviewed and a clinic improvement plan was created to lay the groundwork for what would be a two-year turnaround plan for financial performance. New practice management reports were distributed monthly to each physician in the network so that physicians could begin to understand how their practices were performing.

Improvement of Operations Support Functions and Staff

As mentioned previously, the initial practice management and billing company support staff members were hospital departmental personnel who had applied for the new and interesting practice management positions. This situation was not unusual for hospital-based practice management divisions in the early 1990s. The immediate effect on practices acquired by St. Anthony and ssm Health Care of Oklahoma was poor performance, similar to the experiences of other organizations under the same circumstances. The typical indicators of performance effectiveness, including collection rate, staffing ratios, expense-to-revenue ratios, and profit/loss, were all negative compared to national practice benchmarks.

FIGURE 5.2 Physician Performance with Benchmark Comparisons

Health*first*

PHYSICIAN MANAGEMENT SERVICES   Practice Report

Physician:	John Doe, MD	Report Period:	Aug 99
Specialty:	Family Medicine	Print Date:	09/20/99
Clinic:	Family Practice Center	Pract Admin:	Donna D.
Cost Center:	8547	Months in FY:	8
Fiscal Year:	1999	Tenure (Yrs)	5.1
Contract:	Employment	Phys FTE:	1.0

	Current Month			Fiscal Year-to-Date		
	Aug 99	PSR Benchmark		Annualized	PSR Benchmark	
Key Measures	Physician	50th %tile	75th %tile	Physician	50th %tile	75th %tile
Revenue Summary						
Gross Charges	50,198	33,333	39,583	511,925	400,000	475,000
Adjustments	10,935	4,183	6,538	113,136	50,200	78,450
Net Revenue	39,264	29,150	33,046	398,789	349,800	396,550
Net Receipts	33,609	27,500	32,083	362,548	330,000	385,000
Performance Indicators						
Operational						
Total Ambulatory Visits	495	452	520	5,066	5,424	6,240
New Patients	41	40	80	368	480	960
Established Patients	454					
New Patients (%)	8%	9%	15%	7%	9%	15%
Visits Per Day	23	23	26			
Hospital Discharges	0			0		
Physician PTO	0			24		
Clinic Staffing Ratio	4.4	3.5	4.5	4.1	3.5	4.5
Financial						
Gross A/R Collection %	67%	76%	81%	71%	76%	81%
Net A/R Collection %	86%	94%	97%	91%	94%	97%
A/R Ratio	2.8	2.0	2.3	2.5	2.0	2.3
A/R > 90 Days	56%	30%	32%	52%	30%	32%
Adjustment %	22%	20%	23%	22%	20%	23%
Avg Charge Per Visit	$101	$74	$76	$101	$74	$76
Avg Net Rev Per Visit	$79	$64	$64	$79	$64	$64
Avg Net Receipt Per Visit	$68	$61	$62	$72	$61	$62
Clinic Payor Mix						
Medicare	7%	19%	35%	9%	19%	35%
Medicaid	0%	6%	15%	0%	6%	15%
Managed Care	31%	35%	60%	28%	35%	60%
Capitation	1%	5%	15%	1%	5%	15%
Clinic Ancillary Production						
Laboratory Charges %	31%	14%	16%	29%	14%	16%
Radiology Charges %	0%	3%	5%	0%	3%	5%

Coding Analysis YTD
HCFA National Avg
Black - Physician
Gray - Benchmark

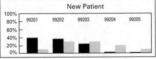
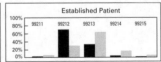

To improve financial performance and regain the respect of physician partners who had grown angry with the organization's performance, Health*first* recognized the need to focus on two key initiatives:

1. Enhance the quality of practice management support staff, which was inexperienced because the employees had backgrounds in hospital rather than practice management.
2. Demonstrate an improvement in Health*first*'s performance and the performance of its physicians relative to national norms.

This effort began with the creation of a policy with requirements that vacant support staff jobs be filled by those experienced in the physician practice management industry. In working together with its physician partners, Health*first* has dramatically improved the quality of its management support staff and the work produced by that staff.

Alignment of Economic Incentives Between Physicians and the System

Health*first* had fallen into the same trap as many other physician networks by developing a reputation for entering into physician relationships with revenue-generating goals but failing to address issues of trust, confidence, and long-term goals with physician partners. The organization initially thought this shortcoming could be overcome by offering physicians an equity position in the management services organization Health*first* had created to operate the physician enterprise. However, the owned and managed practices were suffering and would continue to suffer for some period of time; such significant losses could not have been borne by a physician-ownership group.

Operational Expectations

It became evident early on that Health*first* would not gain enough physician support to buy into a new corporation so heavily laden with practice losses from practice contracts that could not be economically viable. This development was a major disappointment to the system, since it was evident that the only way to ultimately curb practice losses would be to align the incentives of the physician partners to replicate the private practice mentality that non–system-aligned physicians possessed.

As an alternate approach, the organization changed its structure to one that mimicked the qualities of an equity model management services organization without placing the initial founding physicians at significant financial risk from activities and contracts that they had no opportunity to change. The structure, which is still being used, is one that provides each practicing physician with the "feel" of private practice. For example, physicians who enter into management agreements with Health*first* find that their management partner only retains revenues sufficient to cover day-to-day operating expenditures including nonoperating expenses such as depreciation and amortization. Health*first* is the physicians' practice manager, and as such provides all practice management services for physicians for an agreed-upon fee paid to the management company each month via thresholds established in the physician's contract with Health*first*. The physicians see their practice income statements each month and thus know their financial status, including any revenues (profits) retained by the management company. If surpluses are realized, the physicians' contracts are renegotiated so that the management company does not retain monies that otherwise should be paid to the physician.

This type of relationship has inspired a new wave of employed and managed physicians whose entrepreneurial spirit permeates Health*first*'s physician culture today. Practices—even those owned by the corporation itself—maintain a sense of being owned by a physician group. The physicians understand that they will benefit directly should the organization achieve surpluses at a site in which they themselves practice medicine.

Provision of Timely and Accurate Data to Physicians

Management, under the specific direction of physician leadership, produces a series of accurate, timely, and concise management reports that allow physicians managed by the network to see how their practices are performing. The key to the popularity of these reports is their simplicity. Most reports suggested by outside firms include page after page of practice and expense statistics. The Health*first* reports include no more than two to three pages of statistics (always compared to applicable benchmarks) and easy-to-read charts that display a practice's current and historic performance, as illustrated in Figure 5-3.

More important than the report content is the manner in which it is presented. Physicians managed by the system receive their reports each month along with a phone call from a practice management representative who offers to describe what is reflected in the data. The reports are never delivered in a negative fashion, even to physicians who are experiencing traumatic issues in their practices. Instead, a positive approach is undertaken, and physician-to-physician contact is made by the operations improvement committee if significant or chronic issues need to be addressed.

Focus on Process and Goals

While Health*first* was busy initiating efforts to correct practice operational defects, an ambulatory care corporation was formed to serve as the parent company for Health*first* Physician Management Services. This company, known as the SSM Health Care

FIGURE 5.3   Comparative Practice Performance Family Practice Clinic
             Fiscal Year-to-Date

Health*first*

PHYSICIAN MANAGEMENT SERVICES

Fiscal Year: 1999	Accounts Receivable Aging							Collections %		A/R
	30	60	90	120	150	151 > >	90	Gross	Net	Ratio
	32%	18%	10%	8%	6%	25%	40%	57%	94%	3.9
	31%	25%	13%	12%	8%	11%	36%	80%	111%	3.2
	18%	20%	11%	9%	7%	35%	50%	78%	101%	1.3
	16%	15%	9%	8%	7%	44%	59%	65%	92%	3.2
	35%	19%	10%	7%	5%	23%	35%	79%	101%	1.6
	40%	36%	9%	8%	4%	3%	15%	64%	125%	3.7
	19%	13%	9%	7%	5%	47%	59%	79%	103%	2.8
	21%	16%	9%	7%	6%	41%	54%	85%	113%	2.0
	17%	19%	12%	8%	6%	38%	52%	76%	95%	2.5
	33%	19%	11%	9%	6%	22%	37%	57%	84%	3.0
	19%	15%	9%	7%	6%	44%	57%	79%	101%	1.9
	23%	17%	8%	6%	5%	41%	52%	68%	98%	2.1
	13%	14%	9%	5%	5%	54%	64%	78%	116%	2.4
	51%	18%	9%	8%	3%	11%	22%	75%	116%	2.4
	47%	20%	9%	6%	4%	14%	24%	75%	108%	1.6
	28%	14%	8%	6%	5%	37%	49%	76%	99%	2.1
	9%	8%	4%	3%	2%	73%	79%	46%	262%	33.0
	1%	5%	5%	4%	6%	79%	89%	57%	69%	9.3
	36%	15%	8%	6%	5%	30%	41%	67%	93%	2.2
	38%	18%	11%	8%	6%	19%	33%	81%	113%	1.6
	39%	23%	13%	9%	7%	10%	25%	50%	79%	3.6
	15%	10%	6%	5%	4%	59%	68%	86%	103%	1.9
	5%	12%	9%	8%	7%	58%	74%	92%	121%	2.4
	3%	10%	8%	7%	6%	65%	78%	82%	132%	5.4
	30%	17%	8%	7%	6%	32%	44%	80%	99%	2.3
	9%	10%	6%	7%	5%	61%	74%	80%	121%	4.2
	21%	12%	8%	7%	6%	46%	59%	77%	103%	2.4
	18%	10%	8%	7%	6%	50%	64%	67%	135%	6.8
System Total	27%	16%	10%	7%	6%	35%	57%	68%	100%	2.7

of Oklahoma Ambulatory Care Corporation, was designed to
provide physician-led strategic and ambulatory care development
for the ssm Health Care of Oklahoma system, including strategic physician recruitment, development, and retention; development of surgery centers; physician practice acquisitions when
and if necessary; and other strategic ambulatory care development as warranted or targeted by the system. The ambulatory

FIGURE 5.3   (Continued) Comparative Practice Performance Family Practice Clinic
Fiscal Year-to-Date

Total Charges	Net Revenue	Net Receipts	Total Visits	Per Visit			Adjustment %	FTEs Per Physician
				Charges	Revenue	Receipts		
$1,410,969	$848,968	$800,013	5,737	$246	$148	$139	40%	1.3
$29,069	$21,128	$23,386	410	$71	$52	$57	27%	1.5
$553,691	$426,708	$431,313	6,134	$90	$70	$70	23%	3.9
$1,822,660	$1,287,618	$1,186,287	12,747	$143	$101	$93	29%	0.0
$438,281	$341,917	$344,907	4,833	$91	$71	$71	22%	2.1
$403,286	$208,457	$259,731	695	$580	$300	$374	48%	2.9
$530,208	$406,244	$418,990	6,700	$79	$61	$63	23%	2.7
$540,010	$407,732	$459,056	6,626	$81	$62	$69	24%	4.5
$617,447	$496,057	$468,864	6,569	$94	$76	$71	20%	4.1
$1,374,073	$935,555	$783,639	11,530	$119	$81	$68	32%	2.8
$252,342	$197,263	$199,161	3,875	$65	$51	$51	22%	3.8
$265,332	$184,858	$181,148	3,919	$68	$47	$46	30%	4.6
$188,181	$127,308	$147,203	2,085	$90	$61	$71	32%	3.2
$529,721	$342,079	$395,868	4,099	$129	$83	$97	35%	2.2
$570,582	$395,364	$427,287	5,121	$111	$77	$83	31%	8.8
$321,202	$246,591	$243,787	4,476	$72	$55	$54	23%	3.2
$515,722	$90,724	$237,987	1,968	$262	$46	$121	82%	3.9
$804,948	$661,473	$456,637	0	ERR	ERR	ERR	ERR	2.1
$635,795	$461,927	$428,746	6,895	$92	$67	$62	27%	4.5
$454,382	$362,629	$370,051	6,664	$68	$49	$56	28%	3.1
$100,064	$63,550	$50,024	1,337	$75	$48	$37	36%	3.1
$206,134	$170,830	$176,640	2,687	$77	$64	$66	17%	0.0
$134,849	$102,157	$123,658	2,830	$48	$36	$44	24%	0.0
$83,913	$52,458	$69,023	1,228	$68	$43	$56	37%	0.0
$115,801	$92,964	$92,270	1,578	$73	$59	$58	20%	0.0
$114,597	$75,790	$91,730	1,470	$78	$52	$62	34%	0.0
$337,706	$254,553	$260,950	4,508	$75	$56	$58	25%	0.0
$391,708	$196,186	$264,320	4,564	$86	$43	$58	50%	0.0
13,742,673	9,423,089	9,392,677	121,267	$113	$78	$77	31%	

care corporation also reviews and monitors the efforts of Health-*first* to ensure that it adheres to its goals of enhancing the operational effectiveness of the system and reducing practice losses of employed and managed doctors.

The primary value that physician customers derive from the ambulatory care corporation, other than its unique ability to oversee the efforts of the practice management division, is that it provides a home for strategic activity and staff that otherwise might absorb time and energy from the Health*first* corporation, its practice management-related goals, and its staff. In essence, the ambulatory care corporation provides value by giving a separate home to strategic ambulatory care development and management. By separating these issues, the company and the physician partners of Health*first* are able to better focus their efforts on creating profitable and efficient next-generation physician–health system practice relationships.

With the initial infrastructure of the committees and boards in place for Health*first* Physician Management Services and the ssm Health Care of Oklahoma Ambulatory Care Corporation, activity has been directed toward improving the financial and operational performance of the primary care network. The board of directors monitors each committee as the committees focus on reviewing financial management reports and begin counseling problem practices on approaches for improving performance. Also, the board directed each committee to introduce "best practices" techniques via a monthly review of practices or techniques held by practices that have achieved or exceeded the financial performance goals set forth by the system.

The key to each committee's success is the physician-to-physician interaction, including the establishment of peer-developed goals for each practice. Senior physician members of the committee were appointed to work one-on-one with physician practices targeted by the committee for improvement. Recognizing that each practice and its issues are unique, physician leadership of Health*first* meets with troubled practices to discuss possible solutions, physician to physician rather than administrator to physician. The administrative team awaits feedback from physician leadership and acts quickly to introduce possible solutions. This approach reduces the traditional ongoing physician-administrative conflict that had significantly slowed progress at Health*first*.

The physician-to-physician approach has led to rapid resolution of challenges related to clinical quality issues, physician practice patterns, and other issues that are best addressed by physicians. This technique has also led to a variety of interesting alternative practice delivery models that have benefited the system. Health*first* has found that physicians working with other physicians are able to creatively alter the medical workplace. For example, physicians' understanding of clinical techniques and patient care delivery and ability to understand what must and what may not be performed by physicians instead of physician assistants or nurse practitioners has led to the introduction of physician extenders in environments in which administrators might not have placed them.

Divestiture When Necessary

From time to time the operations improvement committee must address chronic practice problems that it finds it is unable to solve. Both the committee and the board of Health*first* Physician Management Services have formed a divestiture plan for practices that cannot meet benchmark standards established by Health*first*. Benchmark data used by Health*first* are primarily derived from companies or groups that compile statistical norms as reported by the Medical Group Management Association, American Medical Association, American Osteopathic Association, and other national organizations that monitor physician practice activity.

The committee's diligence in improving physician practice performance when possible and removing Health*first* from relationships where improvement is not possible, is evident in the significant financial improvement seen in many practices since the committee began its work, as well as in the divestiture of seven physician practices in 1998. This divestiture, coupled with the addition of 10 to 15 physicians to the network each year, has allowed the system to replenish itself with new physicians. These physicians are prepared and willing to operate in an incentive-based environment and work collaboratively with administration as a team instead of in an adversarial relationship.

As might be expected, Health*first* has experienced the standard effects of divestiture. Some physicians whose management agreements were terminated retaliated by creating competing managed care networks. One group began a management services organization that touts its expertise in physician practice management because it is wholly owned and governed by physicians rather than health system employees. However, the effect of departing physicians has been minimal, leading some of Health*first*'s leadership to question why they did not divest of these unhealthy relationships earlier.

FINANCIAL AND OPERATIONAL EFFECT

The operational effect of Health*first*'s cost-reduction activities is substantial. Losses have been reduced to between 20 to 67 percent of net practice loss in practices older than two years of age, depending upon the practice and its willingness to comply with proposed solutions to operational and developmental problems. In addition to—and possibly more important than—the reduction of operational losses, the network has grown from 15 employed or managed physicians to over 100 physicians throughout central Oklahoma. This growth has been achieved with no increase in total operating expense of physician practice management to the system since 1995. The decrease in practice operating losses has allowed Health*first* to funnel the funds saved into the development of new practices, allowing rapid growth with little to no total increase in expense, as illustrated in Figure 5-4.

Along the way, Health*first* has been quick to address "mistakes" made in the recruitment and acquisition process. Although

FIGURE 5.4   Health*first* Realized Practice Loss Reductions, 1998–1999

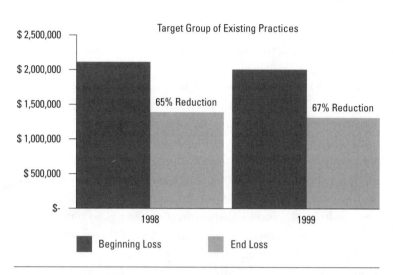

the term mistake is relative to each particular situation, Health*first* found that their most common mistakes included the following:

- Selecting physicians who did not have a strong work ethic;
- Selecting physicians who did not understand practice economics;
- Selecting physicians who did not perceive value in a system relationship;
- Committing more than Health*first* could deliver to new physician customers; and
- Providing high-base/low-incentive compensation packages to physicians.

During the growth phase, 10 percent of the original physician network built by the SSM Health Care of Oklahoma system was divested. These physicians found employment either in private practice or with other systems. The physician network and the managed care organization that remain is a very simple model that is professionally managed and physician led. Health*first* believes such a design is essential for future success.

FUTURE PLANS FOR IMPROVEMENT

Moving forward, Health*first* believes its success will be determined in large part by its ability to develop effective physician partnerships that hold as their core characteristic a mutual respect for the needs and desires of both hospital and physician partners. Of paramount importance is that the healthcare system continues to develop trust with physician team members by enhancing the amount of power and control the system is willing to share with them. Health*first* physicians, as a leadership group, must demonstrate an understanding of system needs, particularly those needs that are important to the system's survival but outside the scope of the physician practices.

Health*first* believes a continued development of mutual trust and confidence will be built around actions rather than stated words. Consistency is key, and both physician and hospital partners must focus on educating one another about their evolving needs, especially those that relate to the financial, operational, and cultural viability of the partners. Health*first*'s future will demonstrate that its success has been built around this new generation of physician–health system partnerships. The organization looks forward to the opportunity to adapt to the evolving healthcare marketplace as a team that keeps one eye on the past and one looking ahead to challenges it will soon face.

6

Case Study: A Successful Physician-Hospital-Payor Partnership

CONTRIBUTED BY

Peter W. Wood, Executive Director,
MMC Physician-Hospital Orgnanization,
Portland, Maine

IN MID 1994, a group of primary care and specialist physicians and Maine Medical Center finalized years of discussions by creating the MMC Physician Hospital Organization (MMC PHO). The founders' intent was to create a provider-driven organization that would play an active role in shaping managed care as it entered the Maine marketplace.

When MMC PHO was incorporated, only two active HMOs existed in the state of Maine: HMO Maine (Blue Cross and Blue Shield of Maine) and Healthsource of Maine. Both HMOs contracted directly with physicians, and risk sharing was limited to withholds on primary care capitation and fee-for-service. The physicians had no idea how the return of withhold was determined and rarely saw that return.

The managed care market, however, was beginning to change. Pilgrim Health Care, as well as Harvard Community Health Plan, were assessing the market. Because they brought their experience from out of state (or "from away" as they say in Maine), these plans were slow in starting off. Their subsequent merger, which occurred in early 1995, further delayed their entry into the market and signaled that introducing managed care into Maine was not going to be business as usual.

At the same time, New York Life (NYLCare) was looking to enhance its extensive PPO business by introducing HMO and point-of-service (POS) products. Finally, not to be out done, Tufts Health Plans announced its intent to enter the market. The relatively benign "homespun" market (from the providers' point of view) was looking at the beginnings of a competitive, managed care marketplace, and fears of fostering an environment like that in Southern California loomed on the horizon. The leadership of MMC PHO recognized the effect of these developments and the need to adapt their strategies to remain competitive. There was also hope that Maine could learn from the mistakes of other markets struggling with managed care initiatives. However, the physician community in general remained indifferent and unaffected by the changes in the marketplace.

During this period, the leadership of the major employers in Maine came together to assess the future of healthcare, especially the cost of healthcare. However, they quickly concluded that they had to focus on more than cost. As in their own businesses, they wanted value: good quality at a fair price. They were not looking to drive down the cost of healthcare for the sake of cost alone, but they wanted care to be delivered in a manner that provided value by eliminating the excesses—which employers were certain existed—and focusing on the delivery of necessary and appropriate care in the most cost-effective manner. The managed care companies were to be the financial transfer agents; the providers would manage the care delivery. Although not expressed in so many words, the employers were challenging providers to ensure value rather than giving that responsibility to the HMOs.

MMC PHO was developed, in part, as a response to this challenge. PHO leadership realized that only through collaboration could providers be an effective part of the delivery and financing of the healthcare delivery system. The self-serving approaches of the past would only serve to invite intervention by the managed care companies with the full support of the employers.

With the managed care companies moving in and with the opportunity and challenge presented by the major employers, the physicians and Maine Medical Center had a choice to make: they could either be the passive players in the new managed care marketplace, organize to resist managed care, or organize to take an active role in managing managed care.

Drawing on the experiences of the rest of the country, they chose the last course. They would work within the managed care environment to make it work. However, only a core of physician leaders, primarily specialists, and Maine Medical Center recognized the need to become actively involved. The PCPs and broad medical staff membership had not become active leaders in the transition.

Forming a physician-hospital organization was not the first partnering concept considered by the hospital. In fact, at one time Blue Cross and Blue Shield of Maine (BCBSME) tried to partner with Maine Medical Center, exclusive of the physicians. However, the hospital recognized the more appropriate partnership lay with the physicians who drive the healthcare system and who can and must influence the changes that would be needed. For their part, the physicians recognized that the hospital was both a natural ally and a traditional antagonist when it came to directing the healthcare system. Both provider entities realized that only by working together could they accomplish the goal of actively involving providers in the coming managed care environment.

Representatives of both the primary care physicians and the specialists came together to discuss how to move forward. They determined that the most effective way to partner with Maine Medical Center was to form their own physician organization, the Portland Community Physicians Organization (PCPO), rather than have individual physicians join the PHO. The PCPO would support the physicians' independence and allow them to meet with the hospital on equal terms in the partnership. The ability to view themselves as equals in the partnership has been a challenge. The physicians have been slow to feel empowered in the relationships, at times acquiescing to the hospital. With time, the physicians have become more engaged in the decision-making process. In the fall of 1990, PCPO changed its name to Community Physicians of Maine to reflect broader physician participation.

Although not codified until later, the mission of MMC PHO was to provide cost-effective, quality care in a managed care environment with providers playing an active role in directing the management of care. Unlike other PHOs that were formed to resist managed care or fill the core hospital's beds, MMC PHO recognized that change was coming and it was better to influence that change than become its victim. This meant changing physician behavior and recognizing that the hospital must change, rather than have only a tangential role. However, for many physicians the PHO was seen only as a way to pressure the HMOs for better financial deals. Only as the pressures of managed care increased would the advantage of a large provider organization become more meaningful to the physicians.

TURNING THE CONCEPT INTO STRUCTURE

Maine Medical Center and the Portland Community Physicians Organization came together as equal partners in a not-for-profit corporation in August 1994. Equal partnership meant equal capitalization and equal representation on the governing board of directors. The 14-member board is equally divided with the additional provision that four of the seven PCPO representatives would be primary care physicians (PCP). The PCPO board maintains a similar PCP majority on its 17-member board. The PCPO raised capital through a joining fee of $500 per PCP and $1,000 per specialist. Subsequent assessments were neither contemplated nor requested.

Like many PHOs that have formed over the past 10 years, MMC PHO and PCPO took an inclusive approach to physician membership. Any physician who met the membership requirements was allowed to become a member; however, membership did not guarantee referrals or a share of any surpluses. Financial rewards would be based upon performance, not on participation or willingness to discount services to gain business. Success in the PHO market was defined by value: cost-effective, quality care.

A formal membership process was developed that mirrored the NCQA (National Committee for Quality Assurance) credentialing requirements (e.g., current state license to practice, hospital privileges, DEA license, medical liability insurance, specialty board certification, etc.) with the exception of primary verification. Members had to have some level of privileges at Maine Medical Center and be board certified or become board certified within five years of joining. The intent was to have a panel of qualified physicians who would be attractive as a network to managed care companies as well as demonstrate a commitment to quality. Within a year of its formation, PCPO had a membership of over 250 physicians. By the end of year four, it had over 500 members.

Following the formation of MMC PHO, the board began outlining the operating structure through the creation of committees that were critical to the mission of the organization. They also sought physicians to volunteer their time on the committees. Over 30 physicians expressed willingness to participate on one or more committees. By early 1995, the PHO had identified the compensation committee, quality improvement and resource management committee, negotiations committee, and credentialing and membership committee. Each committee consisted of physicians (always in the majority) and representatives from hospital management. The committee activity started slowly; the compensation committee was the first to become active.

During this period, MMC PHO recognized that to achieve its objective of being an active player in managing managed care, the organization would have to take on a risk-sharing relationship with a managed care company. The role of the committees was to develop the PHO's own approach to managing risks and rewards to get inside the "black box" that had controlled their financial opportunities in the past. To achieve this objective meant developing a reimbursement structure for the organization, a methodology for sharing risk within the PHO, and tools for managing utilization and accountability for outcomes. This committee work has been an ongoing process and will continue to be so. In this PHO development period, the negotiations committee was setting standards and developing a template for contracts with managed care companies. The PHO was beginning to take ownership of its future.

MMC PHO started with a modest staff, hiring an executive director with an extensive managed care background in early 1995. A secretary and a medical director soon joined him. With the growth of MMC PHO, the providers realized that to manage managed care, they needed to have the same tools and personnel resources that HMOs maintained. Subsequently, the PHO staff expanded to include a managed care data analyst, a nurse case manager/utilization coordinator, and a provider relations manager. This staff provides the day-to-day support for the PHO and serves as the administrative interface with the managed care companies. To help the staff establish their roles with the members and increase their visibility, the executive director introduced a monthly newsletter, and other members of the staff became active in developing educational programs and interacting with the physician offices. The staff members are now recognized as problem-solvers for issues relating to the HMOs.

JUMPING INTO THE DEEP END: MEETING MANAGED
CARE HEAD-ON

The PHO's new and first executive director began work in April 1995—three days after the start of a risk-sharing agreement with Blue Cross and Blue Shield of Maine. The PHO had no committees actively functioning, no provider-HMO contract in place, no guidelines or protocols for benchmarking performance, and no organizational procedures. Some of these critical components had not even been contemplated. The new HMO product, Health Partners, covered enrollees from Blue Cross and Blue Shield of Maine and enrollees from the Maine Medical Center beginning on May 1, 1995. MMC PHO had a global capitation or budget program with approximately 2,000 covered lives. Very few of the providers understood the significance and responsibility of the risk sharing, particularly with such a small number of members.

MMC PHO was at risk for all services, regardless of the provider, with the exception of prescription drug and mental health services provided to non–Maine Medical Center members. For the Maine Medical Center members, the PHO formed a mental health and substance abuse services oversight committee, and engaged a clinical social worker to serve as the intake coordinator and to manage the continued services. For the first time in Maine a local provider organization was managing mental health and substance abuse services, not farming out this responsibility to a behavioral health management company. This move was especially risky because the historic expense for these services was $2 per member per month more than the negotiated risk capitation.

The compensation committee spent six Tuesday nights during the summer of 1995 working through the reimbursement structure for MMC PHO and the risk-sharing model. A major issue for the committee to resolve was whether the PHO should adopt a single conversion factor—similar to Medicare and its Resource-Based Relative Value System (RBRVS)—which would eliminate variability among the providers based on individual-specialty fee schedules. Thus the organization could focus on utilization rather than the cost base for services. This approach would mean that some specialties would have to accept a decrease in their fee structures to support the PHO. The committee also sought ways to encourage primary care physicians to participate, and discussed the elimination of a withhold against PCP capitation.

The committee recommended that the PHO move to a single conversion factor and eliminate withholds on PCP-capitated services. Based on historic HMO Maine (BCBSME) data, the value of the single conversion factor was a budget-neutral blend of the previous HMO Maine fee schedule and specialty-specific negotiated rates. The committee's decision was a significant accomplishment given that the majority of the physicians on the committee were specialists, many of whom were agreeing to accept a lower fee schedule for PHO business. This milestone was an important example of the collaborative spirit that was a driving force in the organization's creation and continuing mission.

The decision on how to share the gain or loss that the PHO might experience took more work. With the help of a consultant, the committee developed a methodology that favored the physicians if there was a gain, but also put them at the most risk if there was a loss. Everyone assumed there would be a gain; no one considered a loss as a possibility.

Throughout 1995, the committees were finding their way and establishing their roles within the organization. For Blue Cross and Blue Shield of Maine, this was its first foray into sharing risk with providers. Its first reports were often confusing and of very little value in managing the performance of the PHO. Thus for most of the first year and until the reconciliation for the first year was completed, the PHO had a very unclear picture of how it was performing and where financial problems might be developing. But the providers of MMC PHO were in the game and were experiencing how risk sharing is often begun and, in some cases, how it ends.

The structure of the relationship with Blue Cross in Health Partners set the stage for the approach that the PHO would take in all of its future contracting with other managed care companies. Like most Blue Cross plans, Blue Cross of Maine struggled in the transition from indemnity plan to managed care plan. Even with its HMO Maine product, it had not developed the tools to provide good managed care information. But to its credit, it was open and willing to partner with the providers in MMC PHO.

This open attitude helped the PHO develop its approach to other managed care companies. The organization exists to partner with HMOs, not to contract with them. "Partner" did not mean joint ownership, although that would come later, but to have a say in all aspects of the delivery of healthcare for the members of a given HMO. Financial risk sharing was only one component of that relationship. The PHO would be actively involved in the utilization management and quality improvement aspects of the plan. The PHO expected the HMO to provide services to the members at the same level of quality and cost-effectiveness that was expected of them.

As of this writing, MMC PHO has risk-sharing agreements with four HMOs: Maine Partners Health Plan (a partnership of Blue Cross and Blue Shield of Maine and Maine Medical Center), Harvard Pilgrim Health Care, NYLCare (Aetna/US Healthcare), and Healthsource (Cigna). Each agreement is different, but each incorporates a partnering relationship with common objectives that include provider involvement in the HMO's quality improvement and utilization management initiatives, day-to-day care management, report structure and content, and financial risk sharing. The reimbursement models vary slightly but all use a single conversion factor as their basis to eliminate cost variability by specialty and provider and focus the providers on managing resource utilization not pricing. The hospital is paid on a discount-from-charges basis. The global capitation or budget and risk-sharing structure also vary by plan, which allows the PHO to evaluate the different models.

Underlying all of the structures of these agreements and the structure of the PHO is the original objective: providers managing managed care. The greatest challenge in the slowly evolving managed care environment in Maine is the modification of physician behavior to reflect the emphasis on providing only necessary care in a cost-effective way without compromising quality. Changing from a fee-for-service focus to a focus on the health of the covered population and being responsible and accountable for providing healthcare value in the community was part of the mission of MMC PHO. The challenge was to create the desire to change when no threat or need, perceived or real, existed to drive change.

While the reality of other parts of the country was recognized, very little competition exists in southern Maine to give managed care companies the foothold to drive down fees to capture volume. In addition, reducing prices usually results in increased utilization where no effective management controls or incentives are in place. The only recognized competitive influence that could affect Maine Medical Center and many of the specialists (primarily cardiologists) was the possibility of HMOs steering patients to Boston hospitals for tertiary services. However, significant incentives would be needed to overcome the loyalty people of Maine feel toward "their" hospital.

Change in provider behavior has occurred, although no single activity can be pointed to as the influencing factor. The PHO has seen its inpatient days per thousand members drop from an average of 250 days/1,000 to an average of 180 days/1,000. Lengths of stay and admission rates have also declined. To a certain degree, the existence of the PHO and more managed care has brought about this change. But much credit goes to the physicians who were beginning to understand the effect of their decisions.

TURNING THE CONCEPT INTO REALITY

PHO Risk Sharing: Integrating PCPs, Specialists, and the Hospital

The traditional risk-sharing model used by HMO Maine and Healthsource consisted of a withhold on physician services that applied to the primary care physicians as well as the specialists. PCPs had an added opportunity to control costs and resource consumption and thus earn more if they managed all of their patients' treatments by intervening in all the decisions made by the specialists. This situation aggravated the relationships between the two groups of physicians. If the PCPs over-managed, the specialists resisted the incursion into their area of expertise. Because the return of the withhold was seen not as a given but as the exception, the only way for the specialists to maintain their traditional income was to do more. Therefore, income was derived from providing more services with no incentive to control the overall costs of services and to benefit from that management. Only the PCP had an overall clinical and financial view of the services being provided to the patient. As a result, the system rarely returned the withhold to anyone and there was no motivation to work together. Furthermore, no one understood how the financing worked (i.e., they did not know what criteria was used for the return of the withhold or surplus sharing) because the methodology was determined and controlled by the HMOs.

MMC PHO recognized from its inception that a collaborative model with primary care physicians, specialists, and the hospital working together was the best way to serve its patient population. The concept of an integrated delivery system was already being developed by the Maine Medical Center Foundation (now MaineHealth) and the system needed a network of physicians to serve as their core. But integration could not be accomplished if the two groups of physicians were working at odds with each other at any level. An approach was needed to align the physicians' shared clinical and patient interests, as well as their financial interests. Then, the providers collectively would have an interest in the overall financial performance of the PHO because of the benefit they could derive from its success.

In general, risk sharing that incorporates the threat of loss and the opportunity for gain can be an effective motivator to bring parties together. This motivation is strengthened when it is combined with data that indicate the performance of the physicians in meeting the goals of providing cost-effective, quality care. By pooling risk sharing with data, MMC PHO sought to achieve an alignment of goals that supported the mission of the PHO.

In the summer of 1995, the compensation committee set out to develop the risk-sharing methodology for MMC PHO. The model had to link PCPs, specialists, and the hospital through referral patterns and use of facility services (both inpatient and outpatient), and couple this information with financial recognition for the performance of each group. The underlying premise in the integrated risk-sharing model was that each group shared in the success or failure of the other two. By recognizing the value of risk sharing as an integrated entity (MMC PHO), the providers realized the importance of developing interdependent relationships to be successful. The specialists' recognition of the role of the PCPs in managing their patient referrals provided the incentive to work collaboratively with PCPs. The alternative to working with PCPs is the risk of being excluded based on price competition from the managed care contracts rather than competing on performance within the PHO. This inevitability would become increasingly apparent as the HMOs became more dominant in the market.

The model that was developed through those six Tuesday nights in the summer of 1995 accomplished the goal of developing a risk-sharing methodology for MMC PHO. The model created three risk pools (PCPs, specialists, and the hospital) that had specific per-member-per-month targets. The primary care physician risk pool was made up of individual age/sex-adjusted capitation paid to the PCPs. In a sense, they lived with their risk pool all of the time by virtue of their own capitation. The specialist risk pool was developed by determining the historic costs for the included services and adjusting them to the overall global capitation or budget for the PHO, which was also age/sex-adjusted. The hospital risk pool (also referred to as the hospital "risk bucket") was similarly determined by historic experience and adjusted.

The previous model of risk sharing would either accrue all of the success to the PCPs and encourage the specialists to overutilize services in the fee-for-service tradition or leave each group responsible for its own risk pool. Neither approach accomplished the needed integration and both failed to align incentives within the organization. The clinical relationships needed to be married to financial relationships.

The primary care physicians fulfill the managed care gatekeeper role in the PHO. In many organizations, PCPs have taken advantage of their new-found influence over the specialists; however, PCPs in MMC PHO are more motivated by the value of a collaborative model that supports the community. This model is committed to paying all of the physicians fairly for providing necessary and appropriate services. Because the specialists now share the risk with upside opportunity as well as downside risk, PCPs do not need to micromanage the specialists' activities. The physicians had the incentive to manage inpatient admissions and the use of other hospital services because they would share the hospital risk pool savings with the hospital.

For the hospital, which was facing the prospect of managed care practices reducing inpatient utilization, the opportunity to share in the savings was a preferable alternative to losing all the savings. Maine Medical Center recognized that it would have to change to be a successful participant in managed care.

The end result was a model that showed patients flowing from primary care physicians to specialists to the hospital when necessary and the financial rewards for providing appropriate services in a cost-effective manner flowing back to the physicians. Based on the consultants' recommendations and the compensation committee's deliberations, MMC PHO decided that PCPs would be at risk for 65 percent of the gain or loss of the specialist risk pool and the specialists would be at risk for 35 percent. This split reflected the role of the PCP as the gatekeeper who determined the need for specialty services. The specialists' share was based on their ability to manage the resources they controlled. The hospital risk pool was shared 80 percent to the physicians and 20 percent to Maine Medical Center. The physicians then shared the 80 percent—40 percent of that risk pool went to PCPs and 60 percent to specialists. This significant disparity between the physicians' share and the hospital's reflected a desire to gain the physicians' interest in participating and recognizing the physicians' role in managing resources. The physician split recognized that the majority of hospital utilization was driven by specialists; the PCPs' role as gatekeeper was more removed, but not entirely, from the use of inpatient services.

The risk-sharing model was recommended to the boards of PCPO and MMC PHO and adopted in the fall of 1995. Despite insufficient data and a small base of members, the MMC PHO shared among its members a surplus of over $300,000 for the first year. The success was a mixed blessing. It was good to be successful, but it left a sense that very little needed to change to be successful. The opportunity for sharing in a surplus that depended on the performance of so many unrelated providers did not affect the behavior of the individual physician. The incentives needed to be brought closer to the physicians and be more meaningful.

Changing Behavior: Incentive Programs

The compensation committee established an incentive program task force to begin development of a program that would put value on physician performance and demonstrate the PHO's commitment to its members. Primary care physician report cards and incentive programs are not unique, but the MMC PHO model is slightly different because it committed some of the global capitation to this purpose. The deduction from the global capitation, in effect, reduced the available revenue for the interim payments to the providers. Thus, all of the providers supported the incentive program through lost opportunity revenue.

The task force had to work through several issues: what would be the basis for determining the incentive, what database would be used, and how would the program be funded? The task force agreed that Health Partners (and Partners One, the commercial version) had the largest number of enrollees and was the basis for the risk-sharing model described previously. It was the only program that was providing, albeit not yet consistently, data that could be used in the program. With Blue Cross of Maine, the PHO had already developed the physician utilization data report that provided PCPs with information about their practice and utilization management information. This report would be the basis for most of the criteria used in the incentive program.

The next decision was the development of criteria to determine the distribution of the incentive. One of the issues facing the PHO was having adequate access to PCPs for new members enrolling in the plans affiliated with the PHO. To be eligible for the incentive, the PCP must have at least 50 PHO members in his or her panel. The value of this criteria was enhanced if the PCP's

TABLE 6.1   Physician Utilization Data Report

	YOUR PMPM	PEER PMPM	Variance—You to Your Specialty Peers ( ) = favorable result	
			PMPM	PERCENT
Inpatient—Facility	$ 7.17	$ 37.13	($29.96)	(80.69%)
Outpatient—Facility	$17.22	$ 20.02	($ 2.80)	(13.99%)
Professional (non-capitated)	$33.16	$ 39.41	($ 6.25)	(15.86%)
Other	$ 0.81	$ 3.73	($ 2.92)	(78.28%)
TOTAL	$58.36	$100.29	($41.93)	(41.81%)

Categories do not include either mental health/substance abuse or pharmacy claims.
Claims costs = amount paid + withhold amount.
PMPM = Per Member Per Month. A cost measure that allows for meaningful comparisons between physicians with different panel sizes. The value is equal to the total claim payments divided by member months. Member months equal the sum of your monthly membership for the reporting period.

Claims Costs
Incurred January 1998 through June 1998
Paid January 1998 through August 1998

practice was open to new patients. The panel size and open status accounted for 35 percent of the incentive award.

However, the intent of the program was to create incentives for good managed care behavior among PCPs. The physician utilization data report (see Table 6-1) provided an overall summary of the resource utilization by the PCP's patients as measured against the expected use of the peers in his or her specialty of family practice, internal medicine, or pediatrics. Because utilization management was a major objective of the PHO and because utilization began with the PCP, this criteria was also weighted at 35 percent of the total score.

FIGURE 6.1   Utilization Performance Distribution Curve

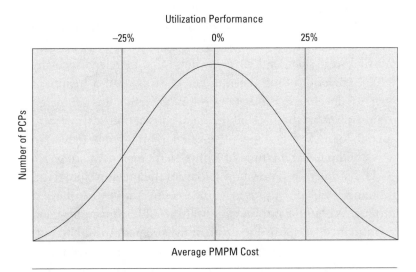

Utilization management criteria were subject to a long-standing criticism of managed care: physicians are rewarded for doing less rather than for providing the appropriate level of services. One of the specialist physicians on the task force pointed out this problem and developed a scoring approach that recognized appropriate care. He began with the assumption of a normal distribution of performance from below the average for the specialty to above the average (see Figure 6-1). A multiplier was then assigned to the four quadrants around the mean. The lowest quadrant had a value of one and the highest quadrant had a value of zero. PCPs who performed in the quadrant above the mean received a multiplier of two. Those who fell just below the mean received a multiplier of three. The assumption of this approach was that the target zone for performance should be better than the mean but not so low as to question whether care is being denied. The model was applied to each primary care specialty.

In addition to the access and utilization management criteria, the incentive program also included HEDIS performance, referral management, emergency room utilization, and patient satisfaction survey results. Unfortunately, Blue Cross of Maine was not able to provide HEDIS data on a per-physician basis. The referral management criteria looked at the percentage of referrals that were open-ended versus those that managed specialty services by controlling the number of visits until a treatment plan was developed. Emergency room utilization was compared against peers in the specialty. Patient satisfaction surveys were applied to the year-end incentive calculation because they were only conducted at the time of a physician's recredentialing.

The problem was now how to pay for the incentive program. Funding it out of surpluses would require the PHO to have a surplus. Without a surplus no reward would be given for good performance, and thus the value of the program would be lost. To make the program work, the funds must be protected in the medical global capitation. In the first year of the program, the global capitation was increased by 5 percent, most of which was designated for the PCP incentive program. This funded the program and kept the providers focused on a lower but achievable global capitation. The questions remained: how to pay for performance if the overall organization lost money and how to accommodate a growing number of eligible PCPs as their panel sizes grew. The boards of PCPO and the PHO recognized the importance of PCPs and the need to set the organizations apart in their commitment to the PCPs.

As in the risk pool models, a link needed to be established between the PCPs' performance and the overall performance of the PHO. The boards decided that the size of the risk pool would be decreased if the PHO experienced a loss. In the case of a loss, the pool would be reduced to 75 percent that would be paid out, and good individual behavior would still be recognized but adjusted for the overall outcome of the providers in the organization. The incentive program was to be paid out on a quarterly basis. To manage the possible loss, only 75 percent of the available award would be paid in the first three quarters, with the balance paid out at the end of the year based on the overall outcome.

To manage the size of the incentive pool, the maximum award was set at $5,000; however, as the membership grows, it is envisioned that the incentive will also grow. The points were divided into quartiles and the funds distributed accordingly.

The most significant problem with the program has been the timeliness of the physician utilization data reports and the incentive payments. To improve the completion of the data, the reports are based on a three-month run out of claims. The results in the reports and the incentive are not distributed until nearly six months after the end of the quarter. This delay reduces the effect of the report and the ability of physicians to recall and thus address issues that occurred at the time. The PHO is evaluating the possibility of generating the reports after only a one-month run out of claims for the last month of the quarter under review. Timely, accurate data continue to be an open challenge for MMC PHO.

A disappointment in the program has been the lack of interest on behalf of the physicians to understand their performance and its relationship to their peers. The compensation committee addressed this issue in early 1998 by publishing the rankings of the PCPs by name and the amount of their incentive checks. The staff of the PHO now get regular calls from the physicians at the bottom of the list wanting to know how they can earn more of the incentive.

As the healthcare market in southern Maine becomes more competitive, the PCP Incentive Program has been viewed positively by the physicians in the PHO. The fact that a task force of PCPs, specialists, and hospital management developed the program demonstrates the commitment to collaboration among the providers. As the environment changes, the criteria will change and more emphasis will be put on quality indicators and referral management.

A Nontraditional Specialty Incentive Program

With the work on the PCP Incentive Program completed, the task force was asked to develop a program to recognize the work of the specialists. As with the PCPs, the task force members recognized that an incentive based upon a surplus that was contingent on the performance of so many other providers was too far removed to affect the individual physician. Reward for performance needed to be moved closer to the individual provider. However, measuring the performance of specialists, even within a specialty, is fraught with difficulties and data that are questionable. Specialists often counter the problem of small numbers with the refrain: "my patients are sicker." Even with the application of a severity-adjustment tool, there is no consistent way to compare specialists. Three different surgeons may have three very different subspecialties or areas of expertise that would differentiate them from each other.

Realizing that an incentive program similar to the one developed for the PCPs was not workable, the task force moved its focus to the next level up: the specialty itself. If the specialties as a whole performed well, then the PHO should be successful. If an incentive program could be devised to recognize the success of the specialty against a target, then the physicians within the specialty would be accountable for managing their own performance.

The other challenge was how to fund the program. Already two to three percent of the global budget was being allocated to the PCP Incentive Program on top of the two to three percent deducted for the operations of the PHO.

The task force determined that the most effective model was to set the incentive program at the specialty level. The PHO's managed care analyst blended historic (1996 and 1997) data with actuarial data provided by an actuarial firm to create targets for each specialty based on a percent of the global capitation. By using a relative percentage, the targets could be applied to any global capitation and converted to a per-member-per-month amount. The actual payments would be compared against the target for the specialty on a quarterly basis.

The task force also wanted the program to be integrated with the performance of other providers, particularly with the hospital. The savings achieved through good management of hospital resources would determine a portion of the incentive. The management of laboratory services was also added to the formula. However, the question still remained: what would be the source of the actual financial incentive, without putting additional financial pressure on the global capitation?

The task force arrived at the idea of using the withhold pool as the source of the incentive funds. For those specialties that came in under their targets on a quarterly basis, that quarter's withhold would be returned. If a specialty was over its budget target, the quarter's withhold would be forfeited to cover losses or added to the surplus. If a specialty was successful, a committee of that specialty would determine how the withhold would be returned. Thus, even if the PHO lost money, those specialties that managed within their budgets would get some financial recognition for their performance because the quarterly incentive payment would be protected.

The Specialty Incentive Program requires more intervention by the physicians in overseeing the data and determining how the withhold will be returned. It is a potential first step toward the specialty capitation that will be briefly reviewed below.

The Specialty Incentive Program was adopted as a pilot program for all specialties in 1999. The pilot program hoped to explore whether a percentage of a minimal withhold (10 percent) will be enough to affect behavior (i.e., if the specialty comes in over the target, a percentage of its withhold is lost regardless of the overall outcome of the PHO, but if the specialty performs better than the target, the quarter's withhold is returned).

Although no money will be saved or forfeited during the pilot program, the program is expected to engage physicians in tracking performance in preparation for the program becoming "live."

It should be noted that the criteria for the PCP Incentive Program and the Specialty Incentive Program were the basis for determining the individual distribution of the 1997 surplus to the physicians. In the case of PCPs, physicians with fewer than 50 PHO members were given some credit and shared in the surplus allocated to PCPs. The specialty share of the surplus was divided among the specialties that performed better than the expected target. The number of distinct patients seen by each specialist determined the distribution to the physicians within the specialty.

MAINE PARTNERS HEALTH PLAN

From its beginning, MMC PHO's goal was involvement in the total range of healthcare financing by either creating its own HMO or partnering with an HMO. The Health Partners/Partners One program, begun in 1995, set the stage for the idea that partnering made more sense than attempting to start up a provider-based HMO. The PHO early on determined that partnering was far more feasible and practical, and criteria for selecting a partner was developed. These criteria included the partner being Maine-based, not-for-profit, willing to share data and information, and willing and able to share ownership on a 50/50 basis. Blue Cross and Blue Shield of Maine met these criteria, and though its managed care track record was not strong, it expressed an open willingness to partner with MMC PHO.

The HMO, Maine Partners Health Plan, would be owned and governed on a 50/50 basis. A similar plan was being developed in central Maine (the Lewiston-Auburn area). Blue Cross and Blue Shield of Maine would provide the administrative support under contract to Maine Partners. MMC PHO would supply the majority of the providers in the greater Portland area, which would also account for the majority of the membership. Other providers would be linked through their HMO Maine provider agreements. As the plan was being developed, the partners realized that the PHO had not developed the financial strength to carry its share without a fairly complex financing arrangement. Midway through the development of the application to the state of Maine, the PHO sold its share to the Maine Medical Center. One of the considerations in the sale was that half of the Maine Medical Center representatives to the board of directors of Maine Partners would be practicing physician members of the Portland Community Physicians Organization. This action by the hospital was a clear reflection of its commitment to recognize the role of the physicians in its future.

The management of Maine Partners and its Blue Cross support staff work very closely with the PHO in the development of programs and the direction of the daily management of members' care. The PHO is kept informed of the marketing and financial performance of the HMO in a way that is not seen in other communities. One result of this relationship between MMC PHO and Maine Partners has been that other HMOs that the PHO contracts with have been more open than usual and demonstrate a willingness to act like partners.

In its first year of operation, Maine Partners Health Plan has achieved 150 percent of its enrollment target. In 1998, the PHO's first year, the organization realized a surplus.

REGIONAL PHO: EXPANDING THE CONCEPT

While the MMC PHO was engaged as a partner in the joint venture HMO, the executive director and the medical director joined with the president of the new HMO to visit the hospitals and PHOs in the service area of the HMO. The intent of the visits was to determine how these entities would relate to the new HMO:

through direct contracting, contracting through MMC PHO, or joining the PHO. One of the hospital CEOs asked if MMC PHO was interested in partnering with his hospital in more of a shared relationship.

MMC PHO developed an outline for the structure of a regional PHO with the caveat that no action beyond a discussion document would occur unless another PHO was interested, in which case the two or more PHOs would develop the regional PHO together. Several months later, two PHOs notified MMC PHO of their interest in forming the regional PHO.

The objective of the regional PHO is to integrate physician and hospital systems throughout the region to provide continuity of care. By joining their risk-sharing agreements, the organizations would have a more stable base of enrollees and a more expansive database to draw upon. It was also recognized that only MMC PHO could afford the staff necessary to truly have a provider-driven organization. The major issues facing the steering committee, comprising representatives from the three PHOs, were governance, membership, capitalization, contract negotiating, and risk sharing. The operating structure would mirror the committee structure in place for MMC PHO.

Although the operating revenue would be drawn from the global capitation agreements, some initial capitalization was needed. The committee decided that each PHO should share according to each hospitals' net revenue, a measure of size used by the hospital association. However, the PHOs would have equal representation on the board of directors: a physician from the board of the local PHO, a hospital administrator from the board of the local PHO, and an at-large member selected by the local PHO board. It was recognized that for major issues, a decision would not be made unless everyone was in agreement. This recognition of complete consensus made it possible for the governance structure to go forward on an equal basis.

Membership in the regional PHO was limited to PHOs whose hospital was affiliated with MaineHealth, the parent organization for Maine Medical Center. MaineHealth consisted of two hospitals in addition to Maine Medical Center, a home health agency, a regional laboratory, a management services organization, and two affiliated hospitals. The latter were the hospitals in the partnering PHOs. As will be discussed below, the link to MaineHealth was part of an overall plan to develop a truly integrated delivery system.

The discussion on contract negotiation focused on the comfort level that the local PHOs would have allowing another organization, even one they were part of, make agreements on its behalf. It was proposed that the members would determine parameters for the contract that, if met, would allow for a single signature on the contact. Unanimous approval from the board of directors was needed if a variation from the original criteria was required. If the board was unable to reach agreement on the new criteria, then each local PHO would be free to negotiate on its own.

Regional risk sharing presented difficulties and brought into question the differences in the behavior of providers from different communities who have not worked together and the disparity in the sizes of the member PHOs. Developing accountability and management of resource utilization requires an effectively managed database with timely information. The member PHOs decided to initially share 20 percent of their risk at the regional PHO level. Over time, as more complete integration occurs, all of the risk is expected to reside with the regional PHO.

The regional PHO represents a major commitment by providers to take ownership for the delivery of healthcare. To have physicians and hospitals working together in a network is a step toward greater accountability on behalf of the providers and a change in the traditional role of the HMO. Initially, the process of working together will be cumbersome, but it is expected to become more efficient over time. The regional PHO will be in a position to sit with the major employers to discuss their health-care benefit needs and the providers' needs to achieve a cost-effective, quality-oriented healthcare system. The HMO will eventually be the "back office" operations necessary for the purchaser (employer) and the supplier (the providers) to achieve the goal of an effective system.

WHAT'S NEXT?

In addition to the major initiatives cited (i.e., the regional PHO, the joint venture HMO, and the incentive programs), which are works in progress, MMC PHO is also planning to expand its mental health and substance abuse management program as a result of becoming licensed as a utilization review company in the state of Maine. Other activities include the development of "boutique" or specialized arrangements with employers for specific services as a precursor to direct contracting and risk sharing with self-insured employers. On a more global scale, the PHO is moving forward on developing an integrated delivery system within MaineHealth and evaluating reversing the reimbursement of PCPs and specialists. PCPs will be paid on a fee-for-service basis and the specialists will be capitated.

An Integrated Delivery System

MaineHealth has always expected MMC PHO to be the core of its integrated delivery system development. Beginning with the integration of clinical systems, MaineHealth is bringing together both the vertical and horizontal services to provide seamless care to patients who enter the system. By developing clinical integration that moves the patient through needed medical care and the alignment of financial goals to support the integration of the providers of care, the integrated delivery system can achieve the objectives of the community: cost-effective, quality healthcare. The PHO will also provide the core staffing for a credentialing verification organization (CVO) that will support all of the components of the integrated delivery system.

Role Reversal: PCP Fee-for-Service and Specialty Budgeting

With the introduction of the Specialty Incentive Program discussed previously, MMC PHO is taking the first step toward specialty budgeting. The model under consideration calls for specialties to have to manage within a budget by using a combination of "contact capitation" and variable conversion factors. The result will be that the specialty will always perform within budget. To encourage PCPs to continue to provide as much service as possible, they would now have the traditional fee-for-service motivation.

The final reimbursement design may not reflect this different approach to reimbursement, but MMC PHO views this approach as a means for focusing on changing behavior among physicians and providers.

CONCLUSION

Throughout its evolution, MMC PHO has recognized the need to be an active participant in the changing healthcare environment. It also recognizes its responsibility for the healthcare of a population of patients often defined as the members of a contracting HMO. Finally, the organization views its customers as the members of the HMOs and their employers or sponsors. The HMOs serve their roles as the "back office" operations that help to link the employers to the providers. MMC PHO is a system in transition—staking out a role for themselves with a commitment to working with the other key players.

Physician–Health System Partnerships: The Physician Perspective

Stuart P. Brogadir, M.D., M.B.A.,
System Strategist,
Elliot Health System,
Manchester, New Hampshire

ONE OF THE themes of this book has been the vastly different needs and expectations of physicians and health systems and their effect on the current generation of affiliations and partnerships. The greatest concerns for physicians in private practice are protection from the many forces threatening clinical autonomy and financial stability and finding resources to secure and improve the viability of practices.

Affiliations or partnerships with hospitals and health systems through one or more vehicles are often the first choice, to leverage their organizations' community presence and general clout within the market. But many hospital and health system leaders have failed to demonstrate a commitment to physicians or a willingness to offer physicians the services and resources they need, leaving physicians to explore other options. Group practices, physician practice management companies, staff model HMOs, and other potential partners have given physicians options beyond hospital affiliation and have been most popular in markets where hospitals and health systems have failed to evaluate and effectively implement programs that physicians want and need. These failures have resulted in physicians losing faith in the ability of hospital leaders to value physicians' worth and form mutually beneficial partnerships.

Although it is clear that many of the attempts at physician–hospital affiliations have failed or are now deteriorating, the new millennium of healthcare affords hospitals and physicians a rare opportunity to reevaluate their relationships. Physicians must be less resistant to the changes demanded by the stringent reimbursement environment, but hospitals and health systems will carry the brunt of responsibility for initiating new alliances. The starting point for most hospital and system executives is a willingness to discard preconceived notions of both hospital dominance and physician needs and begin anew to try to understand what physicians want and expect from hospitals and systems.

THE PRIVATE PRACTICE PHYSICIAN: SURVIVAL IN THE TWENTY-FIRST CENTURY

Although physician needs and expectations vary greatly by location, specialty, age, financial status, and practice style, six fundamental physician needs have emerged that hospitals must be able to meet if ensuring the viability of private practice physicians is to become a strategic priority.

1. Data and information;
2. Contract evaluation and support;
3. Treatment of physicians as valued customers;
4. Facility provision;
5. Access to educational offerings; and
6. Outpatient joint ventures.

Data and Information

All healthcare providers understand the value and necessity of managing patient care to produce high-quality outcomes in a cost-effective manner; however, most physician practices are woefully inadequate at accessing and manipulating data repositories to produce timely, accurate, and understandable reports that support them in providing this level of care.

Hospitals and systems have experienced their share of growing pains as they have developed information systems to support the vast data needs of providers. Although they have attempted to provide information system support to physicians, these efforts have often come with a high price tag and little true value to the practicing physician.

In my local medical community, the hospital recently purchased a multimillion-dollar information system (including potential expansion into an electronic medical record system) to help with patient care management. This system is initially slated for use by only 26 employed physicians and will be offered as an MSO service for other community practitioners. Although the system may ultimately prove its worth, many nonemployed physicians perceive it as too grandiose, even for the projected increased core of employed physicians. Now that details are emerging about the costs and advantages of the new system, attempts by the hospital to offer access for private practice physicians might be construed as an effort to regain some of the funds necessary to support the high purchase price of the system. Often MSO services offered enthusiastically by a hospital are rejected by community practitioners as too expensive, if not inferior to other services offered in the marketplace. As a result, a perfectly acceptable or even superior resource can be rejected.

The information and data needs of physicians can be adequately and effectively met by hospitals. The highest priority needs are (1) linkages and access to hospital patient test results; and (2) systems (including care and case management systems and other practice management systems for private practice physicians) that enable physicians to better manage patients.

Although it may seem obvious to state that systems should be user-friendly, high-quality, and affordable, many real-life examples of hospital information systems have overlooked these fundamental principles.

Contract Evaluation and Support

It is difficult, if not impossible, for the independent, private practice physician to keep up with the subtleties of all managed care contracts. Many solo physicians who are overwhelmed by the bureaucracies of the reimbursement system or concerned about the possibility of being "deselected" or excluded from a particular payor physician network tend to sign every managed care contract with little evaluation of their intricacies. Furthermore, what real negotiation leverage does a physician have as a solo provider or member of a small group practice?

Hospitals and systems have the resources and expertise to evaluate financial and other aspects of contracts for private practice physicians. They also have the ability to ascertain the strategic advantages and disadvantages of negotiating with particular payors and have a better understanding of how to maneuver through the complex maze of healthcare finance. PHOS were developed to fulfill this role; however, in my experience, many physicians have lost trust in PHOs that have failed to deliver on their promises. For most physicians, traditional PHOs are not a viable resource for contract evaluation and negotiation assistance. If hospitals and systems can provide this support through other means and without passing along exorbitant fees to physicians for services that add little value, these services could be of enormous value to solo physicians and small group practices.

Treating Physicians as Valued Customers

Physicians in my community consider it critical to be linked to a high-quality hospital and medical staff. Furthermore, in an increasingly competitive healthcare market, hospitals and systems must have the support of a superior medical team. One of the best approaches for retaining a high-quality medical staff is for hospitals and systems to routinely ask physicians about their personal experiences with hospital operations. Specific questions should include:

- Are there hospital barriers—such as hours of operation, staffing, scheduling, equipment, and other operation and system features—that impede the efficiency of your practice?
- Are there practice support services the hospital could provide to ease the daily nuisances that affect your practice?

Visits to physician practices should be assigned to hospital leaders who have the authority to enact any necessary and appropriate changes that emerge from the visit. Ideally, the visits should be conducted by senior management rather than by hospital "sales representatives" who have little understanding of hospital operations and physician practices and lack the authority to implement changes.

Hospitals and systems should also consider systematically surveying the *entire* medical staff, not just employed physicians or physician "stars," to ascertain if progress has been made and to ferret out other recommendations.

If physician suggestions are implemented, appreciation should be shown to the physicians who were willing to go out on a limb and be candid about their opinions. If physician recommendations are not implemented, physicians need to receive explanations that are forthright and sincere.

Hospitals and systems that are aggressive in seeking and implementing changes to better serve the articulated needs of physicians are building trust and credibility and laying the foundation for future partnerships with their physicians. No amount of infrastructure can substitute for a dedicated, content medical staff—the system's most important and basic resource.

Facility Provision

In the ideal world, hospitals and systems should use their resources and clout to serve as a provider of, or, at a minimum, a landlord of, space for physicians and complementary ambulatory care services. This approach makes sense given the sheer quantity of space that hospitals occupy and manage and in light of the many forecasts that project severe overcapacity within hospital facilities over the next decades.

Hospitals with which I have interacted during my career have generally done a poor job of offering market competitive rates for physician office leasing and ownership. Hospitals and systems should be more proactive in providing convenient, reasonably priced office space for physicians and should understand that the value of having physicians as lessors extends far beyond rent payments. Physicians located within hospital facilities may be more inclined to be loyal to the hospital if the hospital proves itself to be a trustworthy and responsive landlord.

Access to Educational Offerings

The independent, private practice physician can feel quite isolated when it comes to accessing the teaching and research expertise of academic medical centers. Hospitals should arrange for educational programs and other linkages with tertiary centers to enable all physicians, but particularly private practice providers, to benefit at a local level from the expertise of academic medical centers.

These programs can include online or video conferencing for continuing medical education (CME) offerings, as well as electronic access to select CME topics on an "on-demand" basis.

Outpatient Joint Ventures

Many independent physicians are interested in partnership, not ownership of services. They experience income erosion that stimulates interest in ancillary services and facility fees previously "given" to hospitals. The economic constraints of managed care make it incumbent upon every community to provide as many services as possible in a cost-effective, high-quality outpatient venue. What better "win-win" situation than for hospitals and physicians to partner on outpatient services (within legal limits) to the economic benefit of both? Cooperation is a preferable alternative to divisive, competitive warfare. The proactive hospital that values its physicians will foster outpatient services partnerships with physicians. If such a partnership cannot be forged to provide these services in the appropriate venue, the hospital might well lose all of the revenue to an outside entity that can.

PITFALLS TO AVOID AND IDEAS TO IMPROVE
PHYSICIAN-HOSPITAL RELATIONSHIPS

Once hospital and system executives understand what needs physicians would like to have met, they should be aware of some pitfalls to avoid and some ideas for improving physician-hospital relationships.

Pitfalls to Avoid

Physicians have watched as many hospital and system executives have struggled with the massive changes in reimbursement, technology, operations, and information systems during the past decade. Although most physicians have tried to be empathetic about the demands placed upon healthcare leaders, they have also witnessed missteps that have directly affected physician practices. Such missteps include:

- Moving administrative offices out of the hospital setting and into inaccessible, off-site offices. Once healthcare leaders are removed from where inpatient and outpatient care is occurring, it is too easy to forget about the fundamentals of patient care and become less accessible to physicians. Furthermore, palatial corporate suites are incompatible with the limited healthcare services most communities face.
- Fighting the inevitable migration of ambulatory services to physician offices. Healthcare executives would do well to accept the premise that physicians are interested in adding appropriate ambulatory services to their practices to improve accessibility for their patients and offset revenue declines. Many ambulatory services will eventually migrate from the traditional inpatient hospital setting. Recent examples include gastrointestinal procedures,

chemotherapy, obstetrical ultrasound, rehabilitation/
physical therapy, and noninvasive cardiac diagnostic
tests. These services are not the province of the hospital
by eminent domain. In fact, most hospitals manage outpatient services poorly and would be well-served to turn
management over to experienced physician partners.

- Relying on the advice and counsel of a few physician
  leaders. Many healthcare leaders fall into the trap of
  accepting the advice and opinions of a few seemingly
  well-informed physicians. Although these physicians
  may do a credible job of representing portions of the
  medical staff or their own practice, it is best to cast a
  broad net when soliciting physician input on key issues.
- Allowing decision making to become a cumbersome
  process. Physicians are trained to be expedient decision
  makers. Prudent business factors can be added to the
  decision-making process without letting it become
  bogged down in endless red tape.
- Continuing to subsidize bloated inpatient operations
  and infrastructure with other service lines. Rightsizing,
  downsizing, and reengineering are all terms for appropriately sizing the healthcare infrastructure to support
  community needs. Hospital and system leaders must
  candidly evaluate and implement changes to this infrastructure to survive in today's highly competitive markets. If they do not, they will be perceived as redirecting
  physician and payor contract revenues to offset traditional inpatient service losses.

Ideas for Improving Physician-Hospital Relationships

Hospitals can pursue a number of easily implemented actions
to lay the groundwork for building trust and credibility with their
medical staffs.

- Make accessibility a priority. Healthcare leaders should understand that physicians place a high value on personal attention and accessibility. Senior-level administrators and managers should be highly visible to physicians—in the doctor's lounge, at departmental meetings, within the community. Executives should also be willing to meet physicians on their turf instead of in hospital administrative suites.
- Practice openness and honesty. When listening to physician concerns and recommendations, healthcare leaders should be honest and forthright about the realities of what can be achieved and what cannot. If a recommendation is not achievable, administrators need to say so and back up decisions with supporting materials and data.
- Share indirect and direct cost information associated with providing inpatient, outpatient, and other hospital care. Ideally this information is broken down by payor to enable the hospital with its physicians to face the harsh realities and jointly agree on approaches for providing patient care in the most cost-effective settings.
- Jointly share risk. When managed care contract fees drop, physicians feel the direct effects on their income levels. If the hospital or system was involved in the negotiation of the unfavorable contract, they too should feel the financial effects. The leaner the hospital's operations, the less likely physicians will be to blame contract failure on the underwriting of hospital excesses.
- Ensure that the board understands and supports the needs of physician practices. Healthcare leaders should arrange face-to-face, individual meetings between board members and physicians and facilitate two-way dialogue about physician and community needs. Gone are the days when the board makes decisions on administrator

input alone. The board must engage the physicians and foster three-way communication among the board, administration, and physicians to facilitate credible decision making.

Physicians, particularly independent, private practice providers, have felt quite powerless during the past decade as unprecedented levels of change have swept over the healthcare industry. Erosion of income levels, decision-making authority, and prominence and value as key players within the healthcare system have made physicians resentful and even angry about their current status. Above all, they are distressed that control of clinical decision making has been taken from them to the detriment of their patients.

Hospitals and healthcare systems have a long road ahead of them as they try to reconnect with physicians. Although there is much room for improving physician-hospital relationships, a good starting point is for hospitals and health systems to make identifying physician needs and implementing programs and protocols to meet these needs one of their highest priorities.

8

Incentive Compensation Models in Advanced Physician–Health System Partnerships

CONTRIBUTED BY

Martin S. Lipsky, M.D., Professor and Chair,
Department of Family Medicine,
Northwestern University Medical School, Chicago;

and

Christine H. Markham, Manager,
Health Strategies & Solutions, Inc., Philadelphia

DESPITE THE DEMONSTRATED deficiencies of the physician acquisition/employment model, many hospitals and health systems have networks of employed physicians in place and must confront the challenges of improving the productivity of employed physicians and the financial performance of physician networks.

In today's healthcare environment, we are beginning to see increased use of and size of incentive compensation as a means for improving physician productivity and aligning economic incentives. We are also seeing a willingness to reduce compensation levels when performance is inadequate.

This chapter focuses on incentive compensation models for physicians employed by hospitals and health systems; however, many of the concepts presented also apply to physicians employed by group practices or other entities that are contending with low levels of physician productivity and evaluating approaches for providing tangible rewards for improved productivity. In addition, although the concepts presented in this chapter apply to all physicians, they are most relevant to employed primary care physicians. Few employed specialists face the financial crises that challenge the viability of primary care networks across the country.

BACKGROUND

Until the early 1990s, physician compensation rose faster than inflation in almost every specialty and region of the country (Moser 1997). Since then, compensation has either leveled off, increasing approximately at the rate of inflation, or, in some cases, has declined. Many physicians have sought alternatives to private practice, such as acquisition and employment, to ward off stagnant or declining income levels.

To understand the current critical need for incentive compensation systems for networks of employed physicians, the market features that led to these networks must be explored. As recently as 1980 an undersupply of physicians in the United States was documented (OGME 1980). Medical schools responded by increasing the number of new graduates, resulting in a 33 percent increase in the number of patient care physicians from 1985 to 1996 (AMA 1997). With more physicians in practice, fierce competition for patients and managed care contracts has arisen.

A logical strategic outgrowth of an increasingly competitive environment is primary care network development to gain market power. Primary care physicians (PCPs) are key feeders for hospitals and health systems that depend heavily on physician

FIGURE 8.1   Percent of Physicians in Employed Relationships, 1994–1997*

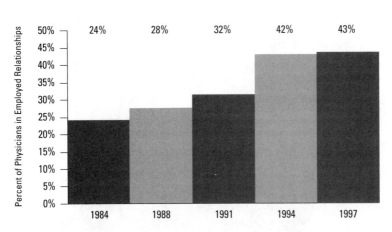

*Excludes physicians in graduate medical education (GME), who are employed in residency and fellowship programs, and physicians employed by the federal government.

Source: "1983–1997 Core Surveys of the AMA Socioeconomic Monitoring System and Tabulations from the AMA Physician Masterfile for 1983–1997." *Socioeconomic Characteristics of Medical Practice.* 1997/8. Chicago: AMA.

referrals. Physicians, faced with declining incomes and increasing demands on their time and seeking secure and predictable income levels and hours, have joined networks. As a result, the number of physicians in employed relationships has grown tremendously in the 1990s (see Figure 8-1).

The practice acquisition market further intensified when other parties, such as for-profit physician practice management companies (PPMCs), joined the fray (see Figure 8-2 for the distribution of employed physicians by type of employer). As the number of potential buyers grew, physicians increasingly enjoyed more attractive bargaining positions. Hospitals and health systems focused on "clinching the deal," resulting in rampant overpayment.

Fueling overpayment for physician practices were projections of network financial performance based on preacquisition

FIGURE 8.2 Distribution of Employed Physicians By Type of Employer, 1997*

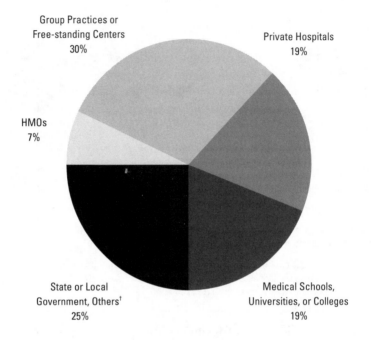

*Percent of employed nonfederal physicians who reported information on employer type.
Excludes 2.8 percent of employed physicians who did not provide employer type.
†Others include physician practice management companies, pharmaceutical firms, and large
corporations.

Source: "1997 Socioeconomic Monitoring System Survey of Nonfederal Patient Care
         Physicians." 1997/8. *Physician Marketplace Statistics.* Chicago: AMA.

productivity levels. Using these projections, purchasers concluded that sufficient revenues would be available for higher
salaries or additional practice overhead. However, as physicians
moved from 100 percent of salary at risk to 100 percent guaranteed, employers saw former physician entrepreneurs begin to
behave like employees, resulting in lower motivation and significant declines in productivity and revenue.

Neither the employers (i.e., hospitals) nor the employees (i.e., physicians) have been particularly satisfied with the existing relationships. These networks, instead of adding value, have become major financial liabilities for many healthcare organizations, with one study ("Hospitals that Gobbled..." 1997) indicating that hospitals are losing, on average, $97,000 per physician per year for acquired practices. Another study (Deloitte and Touche 1998) reports that only 22 percent of organizations indicated that acquisitions completed in the past two years are operating at break-even or better levels. One-third reported significant losses. Although many issues affect the performance levels of physician networks, the factor that has contributed most to poor financial performance is the lack of adequate performance incentives.

INCENTIVE COMPENSATION: DEFINITION AND HISTORY

Incentive compensation links compensation to quantifiable measures of performance. All compensation methods involve some level of incentives, even private practice compensation where essentially 100 percent of a physician's income is at risk. Private practice incentives typically result from the reimbursement methodologies used by payors. For example, under fee-for-service reimbursement, the incentive is to see more patients. With the discounted fee-for-service method, the incentive shifts to providing more services in a shorter period of time to maintain pre-discount income levels. Capitation changes the focus from the individual patient to population-based management, resulting in incentives to provide fewer or less costly services to a larger number of patients. Most practices are compensated differently by a host of payors, resulting in conflicting motivations and ambiguity about the overall incentives.

Throughout the 1990s, a great deal of experimentation with various incentive compensation models emerged in an attempt to improve physician productivity. A 1998 opinion survey indicated that one of the most important changes required to improve the performance of failing networks is to implement incentive compensation (Deloitte and Touche 1998). Incentive compensation approaches include arrangements that move beyond straight salary and fall within a range up to compensation based on production only.

One of the earliest attempts at an incentive compensation system, the discretionary bonus, is no longer considered an appropriate approach. This approach tends to be viewed as arbitrary because it is based on a subjective assessment of predominantly qualitative factors. The discretionary bonus appears to have limited applicability except to reward an individual in highly unusual circumstances.

The vast majority of incentive compensation formulas are structured as performance management programs with cash incentives. These incentives can be reward-based incentives such as profit-sharing and bonus pools, or penalty-based incentives in the form of withholds and, in some cases, in the form of a "tax" for overutilization.

The historically popular penalty-based incentives set up an adversarial relationship between the employer and the physician. Emerging instead is a rewards-based approach that offers a higher upside potential. For example, the base salary may be 65 to 75 percent of preemployment levels, while at-risk compensation (the incentive) could be 35 to 40 percent or more of preemployment levels, thereby creating opportunities to earn 100 to 115 percent of preemployment salary levels.

Experts agree that incentive compensation programs "should be self-funded based on excess savings or revenues" (Cotter 1996). However, given the losses physician networks are currently sustaining, the ability to fund the incentive portion may be questionable, leaving physicians at lower-than-average compensation and exacerbating complacency and mediocre productivity levels.

INCENTIVE SYSTEM BASICS

The most successful incentive compensation systems appear to be simple, flexible, well communicated, and offer an incentive large enough to motivate physicians. These systems also focus on encouraging a variety of behaviors to ensure that productivity is not increased at the expense of quality and patient satisfaction. Physician input into overall incentive system design can help to ensure that the system features these important characteristics.

Many organizations have designed incentive compensation systems that are highly complicated, only to discover that when the system's complexity is on the order of "rocket science," physicians may not bother to play the game. Overly complex systems also reduce the flexibility to reward different behaviors over time. Compensation system design must consider the opportunity costs associated with the time it takes physicians to figure out the program and the time required to monitor and administer the program.

A common fallacy is the notion that compensation plans can be designed to work flawlessly. All compensation plans have some weaknesses, thus organizations must select a plan that is "equally unfair" so that any negative biases affect all physicians equally (Hunter and Coleman 1996).

DESIGNING A COMPENSATION MODEL

Whether the compensation model is being designed for potential employees or existing employed physicians, several decision points should be considered.

- The environmental factors that affect the compensation model;
- Base compensation levels;

- The size and type of the incentive; and
- Distribution of the incentive

To design a system that has the potential to work well in their medical community, employers can benefit from physician input in addressing each of these issues.

Environmental Factors

Compensation plans must support the mission and vision of the organization and be tied to the organization's strategic priorities. Most incentive compensation systems are designed to motivate productivity for financial viability. However, incentives that address cost effectiveness may also be appropriate for a goal of financial viability. Moreover, most organizations value other factors, including quality patient care and customer service. Academic medical centers must recognize and reward contributions to their teaching and research missions.

It is useful to begin with a discussion of whether or not the need for an incentive plan exists. Most organizations have addressed this topic, at least implicitly, but if productivity, quality, and financial performance are at reasonable levels, valuable time and resources might be more appropriately directed toward other organizational priorities. In most cases, however, energy spent on incentive compensation systems is well worth the effort.

Incentive systems should consider major market-specific factors that are likely to affect physician compensation. Unique circumstances may cause an organization to consider variances to standard compensation models. For example, organizations located in isolated rural areas or indigent inner city neighborhoods may have limited options with incentive compensation programs because of shortages of available physicians.

In addition, if competitors are overpaying for practices, organizations are faced with the difficult choice of starting a price war to attract physicians or staying out of the game with the risk of being left with an inadequate referral base. If physicians are particularly averse to risk, they may select offers with a higher base salary even if it means lower total compensation. Continuing medical education is an important incentive in areas with a concentration of physicians who may be lax about keeping current on medical advances.

However, the presence of one or more of these circumstances does not mean that an organization should necessarily agree to compensation levels and formulas that are not sustainable financially. If physicians seem averse to becoming employees with incentive-based pay, other partnership models, as discussed in chapter 3, may be more appropriate.

Current compensation levels in a particular market are also important considerations when structuring an incentive compensation program. It is generally advisable to strive for an incentive compensation system where average performance results in compensation at market-competitive levels.

Base Compensation Levels

The first major variable in the compensation formula is the base compensation level. Base compensation levels should be tied to clearly defined, minimum performance expectations. These baseline criteria typically address topics such as productivity, access, coverage, utilization, financial performance, and patient satisfaction. A clear definition of the minimum requirements (i.e., criteria that a physician must meet to receive his or her full base salary) provides a solid foundation for establishing appropriate base compensation levels.

Office hours available is one of the most common criteria used to define a full-time equivalent (FTE) primary care physician. A network could specify the minimum number of hours available for appointments per year required for an employee to be considered a FTE physician. If a physician elects to take more vacation and offer fewer office hours, then his or her base compensation would be reduced.

For example, at Northwestern University Medical School Department of Family Medicine, a full-time primary care physician is defined as being available for appointments 36 hours per week, 46 weeks per year. If a physician chooses to work part-time at 24 hours per week, the base salary becomes two-thirds of the full-time salary base. In a closed-panel HMO, the workload assumed by primary care physicians may be defined by the size of their active patient panel, typically 2,000 to 2,400 active patients.

Other common criteria include relative value units (RVUs), number of visits or encounters, or contact hours. RVUs are a measure of physician resource inputs in providing professional services and are based on Medicare's Resource-Based Relative Value Scale. Financial indicators include gross charges, net revenue, percentage of collections, and indirect expense levels (e.g., no more than 50 percent of net medical revenue). Utilization indicators include length of stay, hospital admissions, and ancillary tests and procedures. Other indicators include call rotation, referral patterns (e.g., no more than 10 percent of referrals out of network), coverage for other physicians, and patient satisfaction levels. Although base compensation depends on minimum acceptable performance levels for these criteria, some of the same criteria are often used to distribute the incentive portion of compensation.

Physician networks often vary base compensation levels based on seniority, advanced training, or special skills. Other variances could include patient acuity adjustments or additional compensation for administrative responsibilities. The overall base compensation scale should result in total compensation levels consistent with the mean for that particular geographic area, assuming that the average levels of work and productivity are equivalent.

The Size and Type of the Incentive

Size of Incentive. The second variable in the compensation formula is the incentive portion of salary. Wide variations exist in terms of the overall percentage of a physician's total salary that is placed at risk. Most existing employed practices using incentive compensation programs appear to fall at either extreme—very little at risk or a substantial portion of the physician's salary at risk. Health systems that felt compelled to guarantee a high base to "sell" the package or those that competed against high base offers from PPMCs generally feature low levels of compensation at risk. Others, fearing the dramatic declines in productivity experienced by their colleagues' networks, have structured systems with most of the physician's income at risk.

Figure 8-3 shows the potential spectrum of the magnitude of the incentive. The most successful incentive compensation systems appear to target approximately 20 to 40 percent of salary at risk. This level yields an incentive that is large enough to capture physicians' attention, but not large enough to distract physicians from other responsibilities. An incentive that encompasses less than 20 percent of a physician's salary may have limited effect on behavior. Incentives higher than 40 percent begin to mirror private practice incentives and may sacrifice health system priorities by upsetting the balance of productivity, quality of care, and patient satisfaction.

Type of Incentive. Cash compensation is the most common type of incentive, but incentives need not be limited to cash. Examples of noncash incentives include preferred scheduling (e.g., fewer weekend hours or less call time), additional time off, academic advancement, deferred compensation (retirement), and funding of program development initiatives.

Distribution of the Incentive. With the size of the incentive identified, the next question is how to distribute the incentive.

FIGURE 8.3 Incentive Target Zone

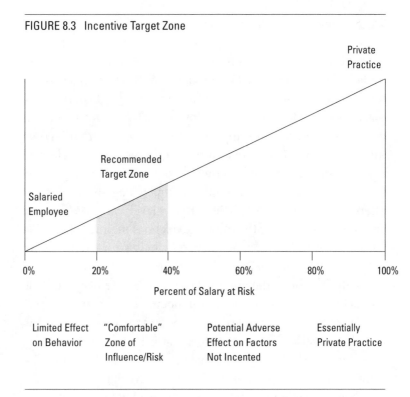

Health systems use as few as one and as many as 12 to 15 measures in distribution formulas. Three to five measures appear to produce the most workable formulas. Fewer than three creates too much emphasis on one or two factors and more than five is too complex to track and administer.

The three most commonly used criteria are resource utilization, net medical revenue, and patient satisfaction. Resource utilization is typically measured in RVUs or patient encounters. Net medical revenue offers some financial accountability but has the often unintended incentive for physicians to avoid patients covered by select payors (e.g., Medicaid or self-pay). Patient satisfaction survey results are used in the absence of reliable quality measures. Other potential criteria are summarized in Table 8-1.

The simplest approach for using these criteria is to distribute the incentive through a point system to reduce the various criteria to a single scoring system. Physicians are evaluated based on each of the criteria and assigned points based on their performance. High performers achieve larger salaries; low performers are at risk to receive lower salaries or exclusion from the network.

Table 8-2 shows a sample distribution formula using a point system. The total incentive pool is divided based on the ratio of the number of points earned by each physician to total points earned. Table 8-2 shows the factors weighted equally; however, a network can elect to assign a higher weight to a more important factor(s).

The point system also allows the flexibility to reward different behaviors over time, as necessary. For example, if a market shifts from 10 percent capitation to over 50 percent capitation, productivity would need to be measured by panel size rather than visits.

As organizations select performance criteria, one important factor to consider is how much emphasis to place on individual performance, overall network performance, and performance of a subgroup of network physicians (often referred to as a pod). Too much focus at any level can be detrimental to overall network performance. Overemphasis on individual productivity may spur physicians to use excessive inpatient services, order unnecessary ancillary tests, and generate inappropriate referrals. Push incentives for teamwork too vigorously and physicians may see fewer patients and take more leave time (Redling 1999).

Some networks attempt to strike a balance by identifying a mix of individual and network or group-related factors to include in the incentive compensation formula. Others distribute 75 to 80 percent of the incentive pool based on individual productivity-related factors and distribute the remaining 20 to 25 percent equally to all physicians or groups (i.e., pods or practices) in the network that meet certain minimum criteria.

TABLE 8.1　Potential Performance Criteria for Allocating Incentives

Performance Criteria	Potential Measures
Resource utilization	Relative value units (RVUs)
	Patient encounters or visits
Revenue	Net medical revenue
	Gross charges
Efficiency	Patient days per 1,000
	Visits per member per month
	Encounters per patient
	Prescription costs per member
Access/ Availability	Office hours available
	Panel size (active patients)
Citizenship	Meeting attendance
	Participation in special projects (quality improvement, planning, research, etc.)
	Community involvement
Scholarly activity	Continuing medical education (CME) credits
	Grand rounds
Cost	Costs as a percentage of net medical revenue (supplies, equipment, staffing)
	Charge per patient visit
	Ancillary charges per visit
	Outside referrals per member per month
Quality	Patient satisfaction
	Health maintenance process indicators (e.g., percent of charts with appropriate vaccinations/pap screenings, annual diabetic retinal exams)
Commitment to teaching	Hours involved in teaching activities
	Clinic sessions
Special qualifications	Number of years experience
	Board certification
	Unique skills/technologies
	Administrative responsibilities

TABLE 8.2 Sample Allocation Formula

	High Performer	Low Performer	Network Performance Average per Physician	Network Performance Total (30 Physicians)
Net medical revenue (100%)	$300,000	$240,000	$270,000	$8,100,000
Overhead allocation (50%)	$135,000	$135,000	$135,000	$4,050,000
Withhold (5%)	$ 13,500	$ 13,500	$ 13,500	$ 405,000
Compensation (45%)				
Incentive program funding	$ 37,875	$ 22,875	$ 30,375	$ 911,250
(25% of compensation)				
Incentive points distribution				
Utilization	3	0	2	60
Office hours	2	1	2	60
Patient satisfaction	2	1	1	30
Quality standards	3	1	1	30
	10	3	6	180
Percent of total incentive pool	5.6%	1.7%	3.3%	100.0%
Incentive compensation	$ 50,625	$ 15,188	$ 30,375	$ 911,250
Base salary				
(75% of compensation)	$105,000	$ 85,000	$ 91,125	$2,733,750
Total compensation				
	$155,625	$100,188	$121,500	$3,645,000

The timing of the incentive is another important variable in how the incentive is distributed. Periodic incentive payouts can be timed to reinforce communication of the performance measures. In addition, quarterly payouts are considered more effective than annual ones because rewards are given closer to the occurrence of the rewarded behaviors. However, some portion of the total payment is typically withheld until year-end reconciliation. For example, a total bonus of $25,000 could be paid as $5,000 in each of the first three quarters and $10,000 in the fourth quarter.

OTHER CONSIDERATIONS

In addition to the mechanics of incentive system design, a number of other topics must be considered. These range from serious legal and ethical considerations to practical matters of data availability and communication. Some of the most important of these additional considerations are summarized below.

Physician compensation is a minefield of legal rules, regulations, and limitations including the prohibited inurement rules of the tax code. Federal and state antifraud and abuse statutes, the Stark regulations governing referrals, and antitrust laws are all important to consider as networks design incentive compensation systems. Chapter 4 of this book includes more detailed discussions of legal considerations. Communication of the overall model, the measures, and the physician's performance relative to the measures is critical to incentive system success. Organizations cannot expect physicians to adhere to performance measures they do not understand or over which they perceive they have limited control.

Although this chapter has focused on incentive compensation, fixed compensation may be the most appropriate strategy in some circumstances. Some employers choose to pay the price of selecting a fixed compensation formula to obtain other benefits.

For example, an organization in an area that is unattractive for recruitment (e.g., a remote area or the inner city) and has a history of adding new graduates only to have them leave for more urban or suburban areas after a few years, may consider a more generous base package. A long-term contract may be worth more to the organization than having incentives built into the compensation model. Alternatively, in highly competitive markets, physician salaries may be driven to such high levels that it is difficult to justify incentive compensation above and beyond base salaries.

Data availability is an important issue for ease of administration as well as the perceived fairness of the system. Issues include the existence of data, the credibility of the measures, the process for review and monitoring, and the extent of sharing of the information.

Acuity adjustment is much debated in physician compensation generally and is a particularly difficult issue in already complex incentive compensation formulas. The typical age and sex adjustments used by many practices only begin to address the issue. Complex and expensive software systems exist, but benefits are difficult to quantify and results are often debatable. A recent article states "there are currently no validated, easily used methods with which to adjust for risk and severity" (Pearson, Sabin, and Emanuel 1998).

The best approaches available today involve some combination of RVU-to-visit ratios, age and sex adjustments, credit for a higher than typical level of patients with chronic conditions (e.g., diabetes, asthma, congestive heart failure, HIV/AIDS), periodic chart audits, and peer group comparisons. The acuity adjustment area will improve as data and classification systems continue to evolve in the coming years.

The quickest way for organizations to lose credibility with network physicians is an inability to fund the incentive portion of the compensation. Many networks elect to withhold a percentage of net revenue to build a war chest to minimize this risk. One way for networks with negative financial performance to fund the incentive is to share some portion of positive changes in financial performance (i.e., smaller losses). For example, if a network is currently losing $2 million per year and the network is able to reduce losses to $1 million in the next year, some portion of the improvement (e.g., $200,000) could be used to fund the incentive portion of compensation.

Many networks are faced with the challenge of managing the transition from fixed compensation to incentive-based compensation. Networks generally use a phase-in period unless the viability of the organization is in jeopardy. This one-year to three-year period allows for a better understanding of the rationale for the change and thorough education about the model's mechanics. This time frame also helps to ensure that adequate systems are in place for monitoring and administration before full-scale roll out.

Network physicians often receive income from other sources (e.g., as a medical director of nursing home, as honoraria for speeches or presentations, as revenue for expert testimony). Networks essentially have three options to account for this outside income: (1) 100 percent retained by the physician, (2) crediting the activity as "production" and distributing the income according to a set compensation formula, or (3) withholding a percentage for use by the network. The third option enables both the physician and the network to receive benefit for outside activity without having to complicate the compensation formula.

CONCLUSION

No approach to incentive compensation is without potential problems or risks. Incentive compensation methods do suboptimize other behavior (i.e., you get what you measure). There may be unintended results in other areas, such as increased office hours to offer easier access, potentially resulting in a higher number of visits per patient. Networks also run the risk of moving beyond a reasonable level of peer rivalry to unhealthy competition among network physicians.

Despite the risks, few organizations that employ physicians will be able to thrive in the future without a clear, well-communicated incentive compensation system that puts at least 20 percent of physician salaries at risk. For organizations that employ physicians, incentive compensation can be a powerful strategy to improve productivity, reduce utilization, and improve network financial performance. It can also offer physicians competitive compensation levels with some protection against the risks associated with private practice.

REFERENCES

American Medical Association. 1997. *Physician Characteristics and Distribution in the U.S.,* 1997/98 ed. Chicago: AMA.

Cotter, T. J. 1996. "Compensating Employee Physicians in Not-For-Profit Healthcare Organizations." In *Physician Compensation: A Compendium of Papers on Current Trends and Issues.* Chicago: American Society for Healthcare Human Resources Administration.

Deloitte and Touche. 1998. *U.S. Hospitals and the Future of Healthcare. A Continuing Opinion Survey,* ed. 7.

"Hospitals that Gobbled Up Physician Practices Feel Ill." 1997. *Wall Street Journal.* June 17: B4 (W), B4 (E).

Hunter, A., and L. Coleman. 1996. "Perspectives on Physician Compensation." In *Physician Compensation: A Compendium of Papers on Current Trends and Issues.* Chicago: American Society for Healthcare Human Resources Administration.

Moser, J. W. 1998. "Physician Income Trends in the Last 10 Years." In *Socioeconomic Characteristics of Medical Practice,* 29–37.

Chicago: American Medical Association Center of Health Policy Research.

Office of Graduate Medical Education. 1980. *Summary Report of the Graduate Medical Education National Advisory Committee.* Washington, D.C.: U.S. Government Printing Office.

Pearson, S. P., J. E. Sabin, and E. J. Emanuel. 1998. "Ethical Guidelines for Physician Compensation Based on Capitation." *New England Journal of Medicine* 333 (10): 689–693.

Redling, B. 1999. "Physician Compensation Plans...You Get Every Behavior You Reward." *Medical Group Management Update* 27 (21): 1,6.

9

Looking Ahead: Considerations for Future Physician–Health System Partnerships

MANY BRIDGES WILL need to be built at the beginning of the new millennium to mend the rifts that emerged during previous attempts to create physician–health system partnerships. Starting from scratch might be easier, but it is not an option for most providers. Instead, health systems and physicians will bring to the next-generation bargaining table long working histories, some that have been successful and many that were not, and divergent perspectives on business operations and patient care delivery. Yet health systems and physicians share many of the same values and there is fertile ground for finding better approaches for working together rather than against each other.

In today's healthcare environment, physician–health system partnerships must be grounded by economically sound principles of risk and reward and the harsh realities of increasingly restrictive reimbursement and local constraints. But no matter how innovative, equity-oriented, or financially beneficial physician–health system partnerships may be, the key determinant of their initial and long-term success will be the environment in which these relationships are crafted. Is there mutual trust among the partners and a shared commitment to community health? Is there open and honest communication among the partners? Will there be shared governance for the partnership? Are there a variety of ways for physicians to develop stronger and mutually beneficial relationships with the hospital or health system? Do the partners believe that their future successes are linked? Has the hospital adopted a strategy of "one size fits all," or are partnership models tailored to the varying and unique needs of individual practices? Are physicians and hospitals forming partnerships—rather than battling against each other—to cope with external influences such as declining reimbursement and increasing regulatory restrictions?

Physicians have always played a prominent role within hospitals; however, their responsibilities have been largely isolated to clinical care and they have had little or no input into strategic and financial issues. Physicians have also been insulated from the important initiatives commonly used to improve the financial performance of acquired practice networks. This role has been engendered by hospital administrators and physicians themselves as both parties have been reluctant to openly share information and data with each other. Physicians who are on staff at more than one hospital have been known to closely guard practice information to play hospitals against each other to gain new equipment or other perquisites. Hospital administrators have been unable or unwilling, at times, to share financial data that would reveal how physician contributions affect hospital revenues. For example, in some cases cardiovascular surgeons have contributed up to 40 percent of a hospital's bottom line (Rutledge 1996). Administrators have been apprehensive about the influence and power such knowledge might give physicians. The consequences of failing to share information and data are relationships characterized by mistrust and adversity, rather than trust and a joint commitment to ensuring the viability and strength of one another.

Physicians must be prepared to relinquish some autonomy and share data that will reveal utilization patterns and other valuable information to hospitals, managed care organizations, and physician peers. Once physicians are more open about their practices, they must be willing to accept the resulting scrutiny and suggestions for change that will prepare them to thrive in highly competitive markets. This paradigm shift will be most difficult for well-established physicians in their 40s and 50s who are just hitting their strides professionally and are now trapped in the restructuring healthcare system. Younger physicians will have no point of reference other than the current upheaval in the industry, and older physicians are inclined to ride the waves of change, keeping their sights on retirement. In return for openness and willingness to change their practices, physicians should be rewarded with empowered roles in structuring meaningful partnership models with hospitals and health systems.

By far the burden of creating an environment conducive to partnership building rests on the shoulders of hospital and system administrators. Physicians have watched the corporatization of medicine emerge—larger, more bureaucratic systems forming with a rigid focus on the bottom line and little appreciation of the crucial role physicians play in keeping the systems running. Although physicians have understood the rationales for integrated delivery systems and continuums of care, they have largely viewed these developments as wars for market dominance with physicians serving as pawns in the battles.

As administrators have focused on the big picture of "systemness" and garnering contracts, physicians have watched their productivity decline at a time when their incomes are already in jeopardy. Operational efficiency, the competency of nursing staff and consulting physicians, clinical quality, convenient facility access, scheduling, and ancillary turnaround times have simply not been priorities for many systems, or at least have not been very high on lists of key issues. This oversight is evidenced by the erosion of physician productivity in hospitals in the past decade. According to data gathered by The Advisory Board (1999), hospital visits per hour by surgical specialists dropped from 3.6 visits to 2.1 visits between 1986 and 1997. For primary care physicians, visits declined from 2.6 per hour to 1.8, and for medical specialists, visits fell from 2.8 per hour to 1.6.

Many physicians have also felt that their voices have been lost in the burgeoning systems, not only in terms of governance and participation, but simply in the scarcity or absence of administrators who actively listen and respond to medical staff issues and concerns.

Attractive risk pool splits, real estate ventures, joint service development opportunities, guaranteed lines of credit, the sale of outpatient services, and innovative employment relationships are all solid starting points for initiating new alliances with physicians, but they will falter in the absence of trust, demonstrated economic benefit, and a shared commitment to community health and the health of the partners.

Administrators must now move efficiencies and staffing to enhance physician productivity and physician relationship management and responsiveness to the top of their agendas. Filling beds and controlling referrals are no longer appropriate goals. Physician-hospital relationships must be value-added—focusing on managing care and operations to produce high-quality patient care at reasonable costs through partnerships that are more balanced, and in which neither physicians nor hospitals try to control or dominate the enterprise. Hospitals and systems must contribute their business and management expertise, resources, and clout; physicians must bring to the partnerships expedient decision making and patient populations that identify more with physicians than with a particular hospital. Only then will physicians and hospitals together be competitive at capturing and sustaining managed care contracts over the long term and fulfilling their obligations to serve the healthcare needs of their communities in a cost-effective manner.

REFERENCES

The Advisory Board Company. 1999. *The Physician Perspective Key Drivers of Physician Loyalty*, 55. Washington, D.C.: The Advisory Board Company.

Rutledge, V. R. 1996. "Hospital/Physician Alignment: A Model for Success." *Oncology Issues* 11 (6): 18–20.

INDEX

About the Author

Craig E. Holm, CHE, CHC

CRAIG HOLM IS a director of Health Strategies & Solutions, Inc., a leading independent healthcare management consulting firm. Mr. Holm's practice focuses on strategy development for physicians, hospitals, and health systems. He has been a management consultant since 1984. He previously served as a hospital administrator at Strong Memorial Hospital in Rochester, New York, and at Clifton Springs Hospital in Clifton Springs, New York.

Mr. Holm earned his undergraduate degree and a master's degree in business administration from Cornell University. He is a diplomate of the American College of Healthcare Executives and a member of the American Association of Healthcare Consultants. Mr. Holm is published widely and is a frequent speaker for national healthcare conferences. He also conducts an annual class on physician strategies for the Sloan healthcare program at Cornell.

Mr. Holm lives in suburban Philadephia with his wife, Karen, and children Shannon, Spencer, and Connor.